Feeding
Your Baby
The Safe And Healthy Way

Feeding Your Baby

The Safe And Healthy Way

by

Ruth Pearlman

Random House/New York

for
Scott and Ilana

Acknowledgments

I would like to thank my husband, who conceived the idea for this book, for taking time from his own work to help me with the research, typing, and the hundreds of other problems that arise when "a mother" writes a book. A special thanks to *my* mother, Jule Himelfarb, who originally prepared many of these meals to feed me, and then helped me put them into recipe form for this book. My children—Scott and Ilana—how I appreciate all the testing and tasting they have done for me.

Ruth Pearlman

Rome, September 1970

Preface

This is a useful and delightful little book. I wish I had written it myself!

A mystique has grown up around infant feeding, and in my practice I find that new parents are very often bewildered by all the advice—and the misconceptions—about the subject. *Feeding Your Baby the Safe and Healthy Way* is an important new contribution. Mrs. Pearlman takes a common-sense approach to the ordinary feeding problems we have all experienced with our young children. She also gives timely and valuable cautions on food additives.

The cooking instructions in the second part of the book are simple and they are arranged in such a way that the infant's food can be prepared easily, at the same time the family meal is cooking, without complicated equipment or difficult techniques.

The author's approach is scientifically sound. It is also fun—and most inspiring to the average home chef.

Herbert M. Porter, M.D.
F.A.A.P.

# Contents

Food and Love

Your baby needs only two things from you: food and love. Give him the best of both.

Preparing your baby's food from scratch—which is what this book is about—will require a little extra time and effort on your part. I want to be perfectly honest about that right from the very beginning. But is it too much of a cliché to say that all worthwhile things require a little extra effort? Didn't you take a little extra time and care with yourself during pregnancy? Why stop now that the baby is here?

To suggest to a new mother that she cook her own baby food may seem to be adding another burdensome task to an already very busy day. You might imagine that you will need an additional set of kitchen equipment, hours for preparation and planning, and a dietitian's knowledge of nutrition. Relax. None of these are necessary.

Preparing your baby's food will be approximately 50 percent cheaper than buying processed baby food from your local supermarket. In addition, you will need only the simplest cooking skills—boiling and using a blender, with a bit of puréeing and baking. Peel and boil a carrot, then mash it and it's ready to serve. Boil a chicken, strain the broth, and you have instant bouillon. All of this can be done right along with the preparation of the family's meals, and once you get used to the idea of feeding another person with his own special needs, you'll learn dozens of ways to use your time in the kitchen more efficiently.

I always plan one or two family meals a week with ingredients that I can separate and purée for the baby. Stews are perfect for this, and so are most vegetables. It really isn't necessary to set aside extra time in the kitchen to prepare your baby's meals. While you're whipping up a shrimp curry for your husband, you can be boiling some chicken on the next burner for your baby.

Many of you are now staying home for the first time and are just in the process of learning how to cook and to manage your kitchen. Cooking for your new baby will make you feel unique and creative. It will also give you the added reward of knowing that your baby is receiving basically nourishing foods *without preservatives and additives.*

Though I am not a pure-food authority, I am nagged by the variety of chemicals added to our food. Are these additives necessary, desirable, or even safe for an infant? In no case has there been a positive statement from either the food processors or the medical profession. Considering all this, I have decided that, although I have no control over the use of insecticides and other chemicals by farmers and food processors, once fruits, vegetables, and meats reach the market and greengrocers, I do have control over their preparation. And from that point on, it seems sensible to me to give my baby the purest food I can.

All the recipes in this book have been tested for taste and texture. You will be working with basic foods with basic nutritional values. The ingredients are uncomplicated and you will find the cooking instructions simple and easy to follow. They have been written to spare you the trial-and-error method of finding the right consistency for foods at each point in your baby's development.

Stick to the recipes, even when you are tempted to season your baby's food to your own taste. If you start adding too much salt, or too much butter, or too much sugar, or, even worse, additives containing monosodium glutamate or other chemicals, you'll be defeat-

3

ing the purpose of this book. Although these additives may enhance the flavor for you, they also may be harmful to the baby. I think you will find that if you follow the instructions carefully, and measure the ingredients accurately, all of the recipes in this book will taste better than anything out of a jar.

Although I have tried not to laden you with scientific information, I have included some useful guides to good nutrition, which comes naturally with the right food and the proper diet.

Of course I don't expect millions of mothers to stop using processed baby foods altogether. Many times they are convenient or necessary, especially when you are traveling. But I do want you to know there is an alternative. This alternative is not time-consuming or difficult, but rewarding, beneficial, and basically desirable.

Your baby's diet is constantly broadening to include new tastes and textures. He starts off with an almost liquid cereal and a small taste of fruit, but before too many weeks have gone by he will be eating meats and vegetables. So this book is designed a little differently from a conventional cookbook. The recipes are arranged according to age groups and become more varied as your baby's growth and appetite increase.

Throughout the book, I have used "he" to refer to your baby. Mothers with beautiful baby girls, please accept my apologies. Whether "he" is a boy or a girl, enjoy your new baby and feed him well.

Here Comes the Feeding Lady

If you have any older children, you have noticed how many times a day they open the refrigerator door to see what you have baked or brought home for them to eat. On Saturdays and Sundays, with Daddy at home, the cookie jar and the refrigerator are rarely closed. It seems to me that I defrost the freezer every Monday morning. Then, when I go into the room where the bird and the turtles live, the bird chirps for seed and the turtles clamber off their rock and go smashing into the side of the tank as soon as I get close enough for them to see me. Even things that are small and green know that I bring good things to eat. With everyone looking to me for breakfast, lunch and dinner, plus in-between snacks, I have bestowed upon myself the ex-ecutive title of The Feeding Lady. Being his private Feeding Lady is, of course, your main role in your new infant's life. When he isn't sleeping, he'll be eating. Although the quantities of food he needs from you are small, his feeding times will be the most pleasurable moments of the day for both of you. And it is only natural that he will associate a sense of joy and security with your presence. Be calm and relaxed while feeding your baby, and forget all the other chores.

They will wait (sometimes for days). When your baby is older and able to eat from a spoon, he will wait for each bite with breathless excitement. At this point, your involvement should become even greater by making mealtime "fun-time" with smiles and babble. You will be expressing love in many other ways, but the significance of "eating" and "love" are so interchangeable at this age that it is important to approach each meal with warmth, laughter, and affection.

While you are in the hospital, the nurses are elated when the baby takes two whole ounces. Often, he will fall asleep after drinking an ounce or less, though perhaps a tiny squeeze will wake him to drink a little more.

When you go home, and are on your own for the first time, you can start by putting three ounces of formula in each bottle. Don't be concerned if the baby doesn't finish it all, and don't save it for later. Use a fresh bottle for each feeding, and soon enough, he'll not only finish each bottle but he'll want even more. Then it will be time to add another ounce to each feeding.

How often do you feed a baby? Be flexible. A new baby who weighed seven or eight pounds at birth may be able to go four hours between feedings. If your baby weighed less than six pounds, he may eat less at each feeding than a larger baby, and he will need to be fed every three hours or so. But it won't take long for you to relax and settle into a schedule that is comfortable for both of you.

While an infant is less than six weeks old, he wakes only to eat or because he is uncomfortable. If he wakes two hours or less after his last feeding, let him fuss a little—he may go back to sleep. If he continues to fuss, pick him up to see if he needs to burp. If he should start to cry in earnest, I would feed him, but feedings every two hours are much too close. If this becomes a habit, call your doctor. He'll be able to help you figure out the best solution. It may be that his formula needs to be changed, or there may be some other simple problem.

By the time he's two or three months old, your baby will stay awake for longer periods during the day and he will soon sleep through the 2 a.m. feeding. When that happens, just divide the total amount of formula among five bottles instead of six.

When the baby is brand new, he will cry before each feeding until the nipple is popped into his mouth. But before very long he will become aware of your attention. He will still cry when he wakes to let you know that he is hungry, but he will stop when you pick him up and he hears the now familiar click of the refrigerator door. At that point I share with you my title, The Feeding Lady.

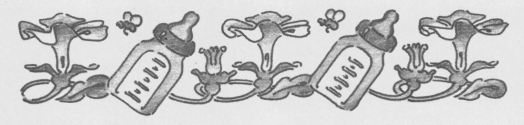

First Feedings

When you leave the hospital, you will take with you a small slip of paper giving the instructions for making your baby's formula if you are going to bottle-feed. The times for feeding will be spaced exactly four hours apart. Well, that slip of paper has no magical powers. Follow the instructions for making the formula, but after that, the rules may fall apart. Even though your baby was brought to you for feeding every four hours in the hospital, it doesn't mean that he slept from one feeding to the next. It is more than likely that your baby cried during the four-hour intervals, and the nurse pacified him with a little water.

At first it will be hard to predict exactly when your baby will want to be fed. He may be hungry at any time from two and a half to four hours after the last feeding—right around the clock. If you can't maintain a strict four-hour schedule, don't get upset. You're not doing anything wrong in varying the feeding times, and there's nothing wrong with your baby if his appetite isn't punctual.

You'll probably feel exhausted after the first few days at home. The confidence that you felt at the hospital, where you were surrounded by a competent nursing staff, may vanish the moment you walk through the front door—especially if the baby is your first. You may work intensely to coax him into drinking enough milk, yet you may not be exactly sure what constitutes "enough." By the time you lay him in his crib to sleep, you'll feel like crawling in beside him. Your anxieties are very natural. But remember that everyone goes through the same period of uncertainty. In a week or two, you'll be very much at ease with your new baby, and his uncertain feeding hours will adjust to the pattern of your household, and they'll soon be less uncertain, too.

Your new baby has the disadvantage of being totally dependent on his parents, but he has the advantage of having two people who will share that responsibility. My husband is a night owl, and he was delighted to take the 2 a.m. feeding, but it would take a monumental earthquake to rouse him at 6 a.m. But because I was used to getting up at 7 a.m. to send my older child off to school, the earlier hour made little difference to me as long as I had gone to bed before midnight.

One very important bit of advice is this: try to nap whenever the baby is asleep. Indulge yourself and learn to sleep at strange hours. Take care of your baby and his laundry, and everything else will take care of itself. Curtail the number of visitors until you really feel rested, and banish the ones that you find very tiring. You may be numb with fatigue for the first few days, but this is soon forgotten, and, very quickly, the thought of having more babies won't sound like such a bad idea.

Breast Feeding

Before your baby is born, you will have made the decision of whether to breast-feed or bottle-feed. This decision must be based upon your own desires. Your doctor will be able to give you the medical reasoning on both sides of the question, and your mother or your friends, or the hospital nurses, may also have some good advice. But ultimately you will have to sift through all this information and make your own decision, without any outside pressure.

Either breast feeding or bottle feeding will be satisfactory to your baby as long as you feel confident and right about it. Most mothers will have a sufficient supply of milk if they want to breast-feed; and, on the other hand, most babies will thrive on a standard formula. Your own feelings are really the most important deciding factor.

Breast feeding has several definite advantages. Breast milk usually agrees with the baby, it is nutritionally unsurpassed, and it is always ready at the proper temperature. There's none of the washing, measuring, cooking, and boiling that is required with bottle feeding. I am not a psychologist, but I feel that quietly snuggling your baby, and feeding him the way nature intended, must give any new mother a tremendous amount of pleasure and satisfaction.

Breast feeding has another marvelous benefit for the mother. It causes the uterus to contract, so that it returns to normal size in a shorter time than it would if the mother doesn't nurse—in other words, you get your figure back a little sooner. It isn't necessary for you to gain an ounce while breast feeding, so scratch that old excuse. Your diet should include at least one quart of milk a day, one egg a day, lean meat or fish, green leafy vegetables, and citrus fruits. You also need whole-grain or enriched bread and cereal to supply vitamin B. Go easy on the Danish pastry, ice cream, luscious desserts, and candy if the numbers on the scale are going up.

Breast feeding eliminates the necessity of sterilizing bottles, but feeding-time hygiene is still important. It's so obvious, but it is often overlooked: always wash your hands and nipples with soap and water, and rinse well, before feeding the baby. Find a comfortable chair and prop a pillow under your arm. Being calm and relaxed is more important when breast-feeding than bottle-feeding because the flow of milk can be affected if you're tense and upset. Some mothers prefer lying down, others like to sit up with their feet off the floor. I enjoyed relaxing in a rocking chair.

Lift the breast with your hand so that the baby can get the nipple and the surrounding darker area, called the areola, into his mouth. In the areola are the reservoirs which, when pressed, push the milk through the nipple. If the baby sucks on the nipple only, he won't get much milk.

Most of your milk supply will be gone in ten to fifteen minutes, but the baby may want a few extra minutes just for sucking. Since you can't see the ounces disappear, you must rely on seeing and sensing that the baby's hunger has been satisfied. When the breasts have been completely emptied, they begin to fill again, producing an increased amount of milk to meet the baby's growing demand.

Alternate between breasts from feeding to feeding—that is, if you started with the left breast at the 2 p.m. feeding, offer the right breast at 6 p.m. If it is necessary to offer both breasts at each feeding, the second breast will usually not be completely emptied, so offer that breast first at the next feeding. If you think you may forget which was which, attach a small safety pin to your bra strap as a reminder.

For the first three or four days after the baby is born, the breasts secrete colostrum, a deep-yellow fluid that differs quite markedly from true milk. Even though it isn't true milk, it is excellent for your baby, as it is rich in protein and minerals. The flow of colostrum gradually decreases after the milk comes in, and it is not until the end of the first month that the milk becomes uniform in content. During this period there is a gradual decrease in protein and mineral content, and a rise in fat and sugar. Mother's milk doesn't resemble cow's milk at all. It is much thinner and has a bluish cast, but this does not mean it isn't nourishing enough for your baby.

For various reasons you may occasionally need to remove the milk from your breasts by hand. There will be times when you miss a feeding because of a social engagement or out of dire necessity. It is perfectly all right for the babysitter to substitute a feeding of canned formula at such times. Or, if you have the time to plan ahead, it's feasible to transfer your breast milk into a sterile bottle and refrigerate it for future use. Consult your doctor for instructions, or call a visiting nurse to help you.

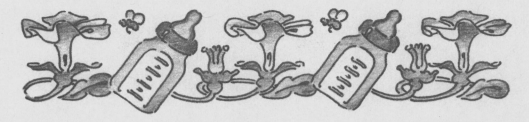

Bottle Feeding

Though it would be very difficult to improve on human milk for babies, you may still hesitate. This is understandable, since our culture does not prepare us, in most cases, to feel completely natural about breast feeding. Most mothers these days choose not to breast-feed. They may feel that it's inconvenient, or that the schedule ties them down around the clock; or they just may not feel comfortable about the whole idea. I don't think I would be wrong to say that for all these reasons formulas were invented and bottle feeding became popular enough to create an entire industry. The most important consideration is nutrition, and in content all formulas are very close to mother's milk.

Before you leave the hospital your doctor will give you a specific formula for your baby. Don't worry. The formula will not be a complicated concoction. Nearly all formulas are basically the same: simple combinations of cow's milk, water, and sugar.

The most popular formulas are those that are already made up for you. You can buy them at the supermarket or the drugstore under various brand names. They are available in liquid or powder form.

The liquid is a concentrate to which you add an equal amount of sterile water. If you use the powder, you have to mix it with the amount of sterile water specified by your doctor. Formulas also come pre-mixed in quart cans, ready to pour into sterilized bottles. Check the discount drugstore for canned formulas. You really can save money.

The most convenient formula, and by far the most expensive, comes prepackaged in nursettes—you just provide nipples and screw-on caps. Many hospitals use nursettes, and your hospital may give you several of the four-ounce size to take home for the first few feedings. I found these were marvelous to have on hand during the first hectic weeks when the baby cried in the middle of the night. As they can be stored at room temperature, you can feed the baby immediately, avoiding anxious moments for both of you. It is a good idea to save a few of these four-ounce bottles for juice and water.

When you feed your baby, sit in a comfortable chair with a pillow under your arm, or rest your elbow on the arm of the chair. In this way you can snuggle the baby close, making him feel secure, and at the same time get a few minutes to sit and relax comfortably yourself. There aren't many of these minutes in the day, so enjoy them. Hold the bottle tilted at an angle so that the nipple is always filled. When the baby doesn't seem to want any more, you should stop nursing and try to burp him.

A baby will always swallow some air while feeding and it will rapidly fill his stomach. This is very uncomfortable for him, and it also cancels out his desire to take more food. The stomach feels full even though half of its contents may be air—like a balloon filled with half water and half air.

Burping your baby means releasing the trapped air in his stomach. The easiest method of burping is to hold him upright over your shoulder or in your lap, with his head and chest supported by your hand; then pat him gently on the back. You can also lay him face down across your lap and gently tap his back until the pressure is relieved. If and when that uncomfortable burp comes up (sometimes the baby will simply bring it up himself later on), offer him the rest of the bottle. If he doesn't want any more, don't push it; babies know when they are full.

There's Milk
...and Then There's Milk

Milk is such a familiar drink that we rarely stop to think about the many different kinds there are. Now that there is a baby in the house, it is useful to know a little more about the many ways milk is prepared.

Evaporated milk is whole milk from which slightly more than half the water has been removed. Do not confuse it with condensed milk, which has sugar added, and is much too sweet for an infant. Evaporated milk can also be used for the baby's formula. It is easy to digest, and has been homogenized and fortified with vitamin D. It is just as nourishing as canned formulas but much less expensive.

For babies who are allergic to milk there are many substitutes. A soybean formula is the most popular. Remember that nonallergenic formulas are thick, so that you will have to enlarge the nipple holes by pushing the tip of a hot needle back and forth through them.

Regular milk, straight from the dairy or grocery store, may be given to the baby after he is three months old unless your doctor advises otherwise. Almost all milk sold in the United States is pasteurized; this heating process kills any harmful bacteria before the milk is bottled. The homogenizing process breaks up the fat globules, so that the butterfat is evenly dispersed throughout the milk. Skim milk is practically fat-free, so it is often prescribed when the baby has diarrhea. Nonfat dry milk is another form of skim milk, and many brands have been supplemented with vitamin A and vitamin D. Check with your doctor before you substitute this powdered product or any other form of milk for the formula he has advised you to use.

Raw milk is still available in some rural areas. Raw milk comes straight from the cow and has not been pasteurized. It can contain the bacteria that cause diarrhea, sore throat, or even worse, tuberculosis. It *can* be boiled at home, but you really should not even consider using it for your baby.

Preparing the Formula

It is necessary to go through all the sterilizing steps each time you make the formula because bacteria grow rapidly in milk. (This is also the reason that refrigeration is so important; germs multiply in the cold, but not as quickly as at room temperature.)

There are two types of bottles you can use: the familiar glass or unbreakable plastic bottles, or the newer, unbreakable plastic nursers with disposable liners. I used a plastic nurser for my second child (they didn't exist the first time around), and I found that it has a very important feature: once the bottle has been filled and the nipple is in place, you can push out the excess air from the soft, flexible liner. This eliminates air that the baby would otherwise swallow, and helps prevent after-feeding distress, spitting up, and perhaps even colic. Everything you need to assemble these plastic nursers can be purchased in a complete kit.

You will not need a sterilizer (the disposable liners are sterile and ready to use), but you will need an enamel pot, with a lid, in which to sterilize nipples, caps, and small utensils. A four-quart pot is about right.

If you choose glass or plastic bottles you should start off with a minimum of eight bottles, eight nipples, and eight sets of caps and cap liners (discs). You will also need a sterilizer. Sterilizers to be used on top of the stove usually come equipped with a bottle rack and a 32-ounce glass measuring cup, which is, of course, heatproof. There are electric sterilizers, too, that are equipped with a signal light that goes on when the bottles have been sterilized.

Whichever type of bottle you decide to use, you will need the following equipment:

❀◇❀◇❀◇❀◇❀◇❀

Small funnel
Small enamel pan for boiling water (six-cup capacity)
Set of measuring spoons
Mixing spoon with a long handle
Bottle brush (for glass or plastic bottles)

Nipple brush
Can opener (beer-can type)
Pair of tongs
Glass measuring cup (four-cup capacity)

❀◇❀◇❀◇❀◇❀◇❀

This sounds like enough utensils to prepare dinner for eight, but they are inexpensive and you'll need all of them. You may already have some of them; try to buy the others at a discount store.

preparing plastic baby nursers with disposable liners

1. Wash holders, nipples, and caps in hot soapy water and *rinse well* in hot, running water. You can use your dishwasher for this preliminary washing, which is not a substitute for sterilization; all the following steps must still be completed, whether you wash by hand or machine.

2. In a large enamel pot, place tongs, nipples, caps, can opener, funnel, mixing spoon, measuring spoons, measuring cup, and automatic expander (included in the kit). Add water to cover, cover pot, and bring to a boil, boiling for five minutes. (There is no need to include the plastic holders, because the disposable liners are presterilized.)

3. Drain off water immediately by setting the lid ajar, and while holding the pan and lid with a pot holder, pouring the water into the sink. Allow to cool.

4. Fill a small enamel pan with water and boil for five minutes.

5. If you are using canned formula, wipe the tops of formula cans with a clean, damp cloth to remove dust and dirt. Then pour some of the boiling water from the small enamel pan over the cans.

6. Using the tongs, remove the rest of the sterilized utensils and place on clean paper towels.

7. Using a sterilized can opener, open formula cans.

8. Follow the directions in the nurser kit to assemble liners and plastic holders.

9. Prepare the formula according to your doctor's instructions.

10. Pick up the funnel with the tongs, place in bottles and fill to the prescribed number of ounces.

11. Snap nipples firmly into place and cover with plastic caps. Refrigerate.

sterilizing the formula

There are two methods of sterilization when you prepare formula. In one method, the formula is prepared with clean utensils and poured into clean bottles. The bottles are then sterilized. This is suitable for glass bottles only and is called terminal sterilization because the formula cannot be contaminated after you have filled and sealed the bottles and sterilized them as the last step in the procedure. This method is the easiest and also the safest because the formula is not exposed to the air after sterilization. The second method is called preliminary sterilization and is suitable for either glass or plastic bottles. The bottles and utensils are first washed and boiled. The water to be used in making the formula is boiled for five minutes. After the formula has been mixed, it is poured into the sterile bottles and capped.

✧◇
METHOD I: TERMINAL STERILIZATION,
FOR GLASS BOTTLES
✧◇

1. Use the bottle brush and plenty of hot soapy water to clean the bottles. Wash the nipples with the nipple brush and squeeze water through the holes. If holes are clogged, clean with a round toothpick or large needle. Wash very thoroughly all the bottles, discs, rings, utensils, and equipment to be used in making the formula, and rinse them well in hot, running water. (You can use your dishwasher for this step, but remember that this is only the preliminary washing and is not a substitute for sterilization. All the following steps must still be completed.)

2. If you are using canned formula, wipe the top of the can with a clean, damp cloth and pour boiling water over each can.
3. Open the cans of formula.
4. Prepare the formula according to your doctor's instructions.
5. Using the funnel, pour the formula into the bottles. (This is also a good time to prepare a bottle of drinking water. Fill one bottle with fresh water and boil it along with the bottles of formula.)
6. Insert a nipple upside down into each bottle. Cover it with a disc and screw on the ring, but not too tightly. (If the cap is too tight it can pop off when the liquid comes to a boil.)
7. Place the bottles in the sterilizer and add enough water to cover the milk in the bottles. Put the lid on the sterilizer and bring to a boil. Boil for twenty-five minutes.
8. When the bottles are cool enough to handle, screw the rings down tight. Refrigerate.

❖◇❖

METHOD II: PRELIMINARY STERILIZATION,
FOR GLASS OR PLASTIC BOTTLES

❖◇❖

1. Wash the bottles, nipples, rings, discs, utensils, and everything else you will be using in hot, soapy water. Use your bottle and nipple brushes for scrubbing. Force water through the nipple holes to make sure that they are not clogged. Rinse everything well in hot, running water. (You can use your dishwasher for this step, but remember that this is only the preliminary washing and is not a substitute for sterilization. All the following steps must still be completed.)
2. Place the bottles upside down in the sterilizer rack. There is a place in the center of the sterilizer for your large measuring cup.

Fill the measuring cup half full with water and place tongs, funnel and other small equipment in it. The nipples and caps usually have their own special glass container with a perforated lid. This container is placed in the sterilizer, lid side down. If your sterilizer doesn't have this jar, you can manage by wrapping the nipples and caps in a piece of cheesecloth and tying it with a piece of string.

3. Pour about four inches of hot water into the sterilizer and bring to a boil. Boil for five minutes.
4. Allow the bottles to cool until they are comfortable to handle.
5. Fill the small enamel pan with water and boil for five minutes.
6. If you are using canned formula, wipe the top of the can with a clean, damp cloth and then pour over it a little of the boiling water from the small enamel pan.
7. Use the tongs to remove the sterilized bottles, utensils, and nipple container from the sterilizer. Place them on clean paper towels.
8. Using the sterilized can opener, open the formula can.
9. Using the sterilized water from the small enamel pan, mix the formula according to your doctor's instructions.
10. Place the funnel in each bottle and pour in the number of ounces required.
11. Using the tongs, remove the nipples from the container or cheesecloth and place a nipple upside down in each bottle. Cover the nipple with a disc, then screw on the cap. Refrigerate the bottles.

Don't let all these instructions intimidate you. After a few days you'll get the hang of it, and the whole procedure will become routine and automatic.

Everyone has different ideas about the proper temperature of the formula for feeding. Some mothers prefer to give the formula at room temperature, others heat it a bit to take the chill off, and some mothers give their babies a bottle right from the refrigerator. The babies don't seem to care, but I think it's a good idea to be consistent and give the formula at the same temperature at every feeding.

If you do heat the bottle, stand it in a pan of hot water for a few minutes. (An electric bottle warmer is wonderful too, if someone asks you for a baby gift suggestion.)

If you're using the plastic baby nurser, you can heat the formula faster by removing the cap, pushing out the air, and replacing the cap again to prevent the air from going back in. Then when you warm the formula, you don't waste precious seconds warming the air first. (Those few seconds won't seem like much to you, but your baby will appreciate every one of them.)

When you are heating a bottle you are aiming for body temperature, so shake a few drops onto the inside of your wrist to test it. When it's just right, it will feel neither hot nor cold.

Introducing Solid Foods

Your baby will probably eat his first solid food when he is about six weeks old. The starting time for solid food seems to get earlier and earlier with every new crop of babies. However, don't fall into the trap of comparing the progress of your baby with the progress of a friend's baby. It really doesn't matter if her baby is eating cereal a week before yours, or vice versa. She is following the advice of her doctor and you should follow the advice of yours. (Use the same doctor and you'll have no problems.)

One very good reason why your doctor may recommend solid foods at an early age is that cereals, fruits, meats, and vegetables provide important vitamins and minerals that are not found in large enough quantities in milk. Another reason is that if you waited until your baby was a year old before giving him solid food, it would be difficult to introduce a spoon after he had become so attached to a nipple. (This delay was customary a couple of generations ago, and was the cause of the weaning problems that were much talked about.) In addition, a baby kept on a 100 percent milk diet for too long would look pale and flabby instead of bright-eyed and full of pep.

When you start giving solid foods, such as cereal and fruit, try feeding the solids *before* offering the bottle so that he is not too full to be interested. But if your baby is so hungry that he cries and seems sure starvation is only two seconds away, give him half the bottle and then try the cereal and fruit. In a week or two he'll learn that cereal and fruit fill his tummy just as milk does, and he'll be willing to wait for his bottle.

feeding equipment

Silver spoons are often gifts from favorite aunts, but if your baby hasn't been given one, you can buy a very nice stainless-steel baby spoon at the grocery, department, or drugstore. A narrow, shallow spoon is ideal (and it's even better if the bowl is rubber coated). A demitasse spoon sounds fancy, but it is the perfect size. *Please,* don't ever attempt to use a fork when feeding a small baby.

A baby doesn't really need a special dish to eat from, and even though it's cute, the money it costs is worth more in his piggy bank. But if someone asks what the baby needs, this is a nifty way to get one. There are china dishes sectioned into three parts, and dishes with a hollow base that can be filled with hot water to keep the food warm, and a lovely electric heat-and-serve dish with a thermostat. You don't have to sterilize the feeding dish, because hard, clean, dry surfaces do not provide a good environment for bacteria to grow and, of course, you don't store food in the dish. Just wash the baby dish and spoon in hot, soapy water and rinse well.

The best bibs are the ones with snaps. They are easier to put on than the tie-on kind, and you don't run the risk of burning the baby's neck with the strings when you pull it off. Buy big bibs. The bibs that have terry cloth on one side and plastic on the other can really do double duty. The cloth side can be used to wipe a messy face, and the plastic prevents the dampness from soaking through to the baby's clothes. Bibs with a crumb-catcher pocket along the bottom help prevent a crunchy kitchen floor.

Don't even bother with the small-sized bibs, as they are only good for a few weeks. Babies begin to dribble or slobber (there's no cute name for this) at about two and a half or three months of age. The salivary glands are starting to function at this point, and teething may be beginning, too. During this period, whenever the baby is awake, it's a good idea to keep a bib on him. It will keep his undershirt and clothes dry, prevent his chin from getting chapped, and his chest from getting damp and cold. This is particularly good advice for drafty winter weather. However, you should always remove the bib before naptime so that it doesn't slide up and interfere with his breathing.

While I'm talking about protective clothing, I'd like to mention that aprons are indispensable to mothers. The old-fashioned ones, with high fronts, are perfect while you're bathing and feeding your baby, especially after he has learned to spit out food or to knock things over. And always place a diaper or other soft cloth over your shoulder when you pick up your baby to burp him. Even with this precaution, you will have a white shoulder patch on everything you wear. This is your badge of motherhood (and fatherhood), so wear it proudly. Pack away your good sweaters and your "little basic blacks" for the next six months. When you see them again they will be the next best thing to a wild and wicked shopping spree.

cooking equipment

Other items of equipment you'll use in preparing your own baby food include a small pan with a tight-fitting lid, a small frying pan, a food mill, a vegetable brush, an electric blender, and a sieve or strainer. You will also find that a swivel-bladed vegetable peeler and a small enamel saucepan are invaluable. The six-cup pan you have been using in making formula is a good size.

The only item that will cost more than three dollars is the blender, and a good one can be purchased at a discount store for less than fifteen dollars. (You don't need one with twelve speeds, a timer, four extra attachments, and a transistor radio. If you are on a budget, the two-speed model is fine.)

Refrigeration is very important, since it retards spoilage. Food is just too expensive to waste. (In case you haven't checked lately, it has become your biggest monthly expenditure.) Making your own baby food is far less expensive than buying it.

Most of the recipes in this book make two or more servings. Use one serving and freeze the rest. After you prepare the food, place it in a glass or plastic container and refrigerate it immediately. As soon as it is cool, cover tightly and refrigerate or freeze. This is especially important with chicken and beef broths, because broth provides very favorable conditions for bacteria to multiply.

If you have a freezer that keeps food at zero degrees or under—a Deep-freeze—make several extra portions of baby food while you're cooking. Label and date the containers carefully. Don't keep cooked meat frozen longer than two to three months, or cooked fruits and vegetables frozen longer than ten months. (This applies to your own food as well as the baby's.)

Sterilizing the pans, small appliances, dishes, and spoons isn't necessary. Wash them well in hot, soapy water and rinse thoroughly. Dry utensils, such as your baby's dish and spoon, do not provide a good environment for germs. (And, incidentally, there is no need to melt his favorite plastic toys in boiling water. A good thorough washing is sufficient, unless they have fallen in the street.) Before you open cans, wipe them with a damp cloth and rinse the tops quickly with very hot water.

Most of us prefer to eat our meats and vegetables warm, and fruits and salads cold; and we pass these preferences on to our children. There are no hard-and-fast rules about this except that you should always test food for a safe serving temperature for your baby; it should be neither too hot nor too cold. The best test is to take an extra spoon and taste it yourself. All foods can be served at room temperature if you wish. Heating baby food in the top of a double boiler only takes a few minutes, and you can't burn the food being warmed in this way. (It's easy to improvise a double boiler by placing a small heatproof glass bowl in a pan of hot water.) If you are careful not to scorch it, you can also heat any food in a small pan directly over a flame. This is the easiest method for heating milk for cereal. As I have mentioned, an electric heat-and-serve dish is wonderfully easy to use, is just the right size, and is very convenient. Just be sure to follow the manufacturer's directions very carefully.

How to Feed Your Baby

When you are spoon-feeding your baby for the first time, hold him in your lap a bit more upright than for bottle-feeding. Hold one arm with your free hand, and tuck the other around your side. This is not uncomfortable for the baby, and it does eliminate the mess caused when a tiny, waving hand meets the feeding spoon.

You can also use a reclining plastic infant seat as a first "high chair." Some mothers use them right from the very beginning. Using the seat frees both of your hands, the baby can be propped up comfortably on the table in front of you, and somehow you feel you have more control of the whole situation. However, when your baby is very young, he may feel more secure in these new eating adventures while he is snuggled in your lap.

Throw away any unused food left in the baby's dish. Saliva has been introduced into the food, and it will cause leftovers to spoil quickly.

You can't talk about feeding your baby without talking about laundry. Formulas and certain foods, especially beets and bananas, stain clothing. For years I avoided using chlorine bleach in the babies' laundry because I thought it could cause a skin rash. As a result, their undershirts were always a mess. Then a friend, a most perfect housekeeper (you know the kind: each kitchen shelf is lined more beautifully than the last), took me in tow and explained that I could soak white and colorfast baby clothes in a solution of one cup of chlorine bleach and six cups of water for thirty minutes. After thorough rinsing, the clothes were then washed as usual in the washing machine. If I could still detect a faint odor of the chlorine bleach, I'd reset the dial and rinse a second time. Of course, this treatment is not necessary every time you wash bibs or other food-stained baby clothes—just once in a while when the stains become unbearable.

Changes in Appetite

During his first year, your baby will have a mighty appetite. You may wonder where he's putting all that food by the time he's nine or ten months of age. But babies are incredibly active, learning to sit, to pull themselves up, then to crawl around behind you, and finally to walk. Activity, coupled with rapid growth, is calorie-consuming, and his appetite will prove it. In the average baby, appetite and growth go hand in hand.

Your baby's appetite will continue to increase until he is almost two years old. Somewhere between two and three years of age, there may be a sharp reduction in his appetite, even though his activities are increasing. This is nothing to worry about. Though his activity is increasing, his rate of growth is slowing down. He needs less food, and quite sensibly, he'll eat less. Make sure to include plenty of meat, fish, and eggs in his diet for body building at that stage. Vitamin tablets and drops are essential preparations, but they cannot substitute for three good meals a day. Your baby needs the high-protein meals to ensure proper nutrition.

Usually, you can expect a "vegetable strike" at this age, so try raw and cooked fruits instead. You'll find that your toddler will have strong likes and dislikes and will go hungry rather than eat something he "hates." Don't fret about it. There is plenty of time for him to become a gourmet. Proper nutrition is more important, so offer him the meats and vegetables that he does like, often.

Additives

Every now and again there is a controversy about food additives. There are some additives that are beneficial and some that are highly questionable. Some foods are fortified with vitamins and minerals. For example, bread is enriched with vitamins and minerals; vitamin A is added to margarine; and table salt is iodized. All these additives are considered helpful. Vitamin D is not found in milk in its original state, but since it is so important to ensure strong bones, it is added to the one drink that babies and children consume in great quantities. However, even though vitamin D has almost eliminated rickets in the United States, there is now some concern that it might, in very large doses, cause calcium deposits.

Many additives are included in commercial baby foods to make them taste better to the mother, or to make them keep longer. I repeat again, that although these additives enhance the flavor for adults, they may be harmful for a baby. Monosodium glutamate, salt, and carboxyl methyl cellulose are examples. Evidence is accumulating that suggests a correlation between salt intake and hypertension (high blood pressure). If an infant's kidneys are functioning properly and he drinks plenty of water, he is able to excrete the sodium chloride (salt) that his body doesn't require. But why feed him an excess, when salt is only for flavoring? Moreover, sufficient sodium chloride for good taste occurs naturally in meats, fish and many vegetables. I use salt sparingly in my recipes, and then only when the ingredients do not include a natural source of salt.

Monosodium glutamate, another flavor-enhancing additive, is under the scrutiny of the Food and Drug Administration. Carboxyl methyl cellulose, a cotton by-product, is used as a food stabilizer, and there have been some indications that it may cause cancer in laboratory animals. Many other kinds of chemicals are intentionally added to our foods for all kinds of reasons: coloring agents to perk up the appearance; antispoilants, such as calcium propionate, to keep bread fresh a few days longer; many flavoring agents, most of which are synthetic; moisture controls, such as glycerin in marshmallows; and calcium silicate, added to prevent table salt from caking. Even bananas often receive applications of ethylene to hasten ripening.

The list could go on and on and on. The Food and Drug Administration may someday find that every single food additive is safe, but with 2,764 chemicals to deal with, I'd say the odds are against it.

A baby doesn't eat the same quantity of food as an adult, and he will naturally consume a smaller amount of additives. But his weight may be only a tenth of an adult's, and even the small amount of harmful additives in his food would have a much greater effect on him.

All additives should be eliminated from baby food if there is the slightest possibility that they are harmful. (In fact, they should have been thoroughly tested before they were added.) We've known for a long time that human beings can survive without chemical additives in their food. We know precious little about the other side of this question.

That is the strongest reason I can give you for preparing your own baby food—plus the fact that the food is all so delicious. I have had a wonderful time in the kitchen feeding my own baby and tasting the dishes made from these recipes.

Feeding a Sick Child

Once in a while your baby will feel out of sorts. True, he is a little person, but little people are just as likely to have stomach cramps, gas, indigestion, aches, and pains as you are. Unfortunately he can't tell you when he isn't feeling well. But when you do notice a loss of appetite and he seems irritable, give the baby foods like broth, cream of rice, and fruit gelatins for a few days. Try to feed him the foods he likes best, and his appetite will let you know when he is feeling better. If his lack of appetite continues for more than a couple of days, there is a chance that something more serious is bothering him. Don't try home remedies and don't listen to your friends and relatives. Call your doctor immediately.

Liquids are more important than solid foods when your baby is running a temperature. Give him plenty of water, fruit juices, even flat ginger ale and flat cola drinks. If he is old enough to use a straw, slip a colorful one into his drink. It may cheer him up a bit.

teething

There are still old wives' tales floating around that teething can cause colds, fevers, and diarrhea. Those symptoms may often accompany teething, but a new tooth has never given a baby a cold. His resistance may be lower when he is teething, but it still takes a germ to cause a cold or intestinal disorder. Yet, because a baby teethes for such a long period—from four months to two and a half years—all the minor ailments he suffers are usually accounted for by "Oh, he's teething."

Your baby's teeth are formed beneath the gums before he is born. This is why it is important that an expectant mother's diet provide the necessary vitamins and minerals—lots of milk, meat, and vegetables—for the baby's teeth. The permanent teeth are formed during the first couple of months after birth, so it is equally important that you feed him the necessary vitamins C and D, plus plenty of calcium and phosphorus.

eczema and allergies

Eczema is the most common skin disease during early childhood. Blotchy patches that are scaly, itchy, and red may show up on a new baby's skin, commonly on the cheeks and scalp. As he grows older, the rash is usually localized in the creases of his elbows and the backs of his knees.

Eczema is extremely itchy, and a baby will attempt to scratch, even while he's asleep. Don't apply ointments that have been in your medicine chest a long time. Again, call your doctor and have him examine the baby if possible; he'll prescribe the proper medication.

An occasional baby will be allergic to some material in his clothing or blanket. Sometimes a baby's skin will break out during the winter, when many homes are hot and very dry. And some children have rashes only during the summer, when their skin is irritated from perspiration. In other cases, a baby may be allergic to one or more foods he is eating. The allergens in food travel through the bloodstream to the skin, and at that point the rash flares up.

The saddest part of eczemas, allergic rashes or, for that matter, any baby ailment is that you will feel so helpless, and he will be so miserable. All of these superficial ailments are usually a direct result of our own actions: it's something we feed them, or something we put on them. If your doctor finds a connection between food and the appearance of eczema, he will most likely say it is the protein in milk. He may prescribe a milk-free formula. There are formulas made from soybeans that can be substituted for milk-based formulas, and they are equally nourishing. A baby with eczema will tolerate cooked fruit and vegetables, but meat, eggs, and fish must be used cautiously. If the protein in these foods causes the eczema to spread, your doctor will probably advise you to stop feeding them for a while.

Fruit juices that are highly acid, such as orange juice and tomato juice, can also be the culprits when they come in contact with the baby's skin. Wipe the dribbles of juice off your baby's chin as soon as he is finished drinking.

digestive problems

Many symptoms of a sickness show up in a child's digestive system. He may lose his appetite, or have diarrhea, or vomit, or urinate more frequently than usual. A simple cold can cause some of these symptoms, but serious illnesses frequently start the same way. Check with your doctor when *any* of these symptoms appear.

VOMITING

If your baby vomits forcibly (a violent discharge, as opposed to spitting up), discontinue all solid foods. Give him a teaspoon or two of cool, boiled water or weak, cool, sweetened tea every half hour. If the vomiting is severe, it is important to call the doctor because it can cause dehydration. When he tells you to resume solid foods, dilute your baby's milk half-and-half with boiled and cooled water. Gradually increase the strength of the milk over the next few days if everything is going well. His menu during this period should consist of bland, easily digested foods.

DIARRHEA

Because your baby's digestive tract is brand new, he is more prone to have diarrhea than you are. Many things can cause diarrhea: bacteria, the same germs that cause colds, or even a new food. A severe case of diarrhea can lead to the loss of potassium and sodium, the minerals needed by the body to retain water in the tissues. The result is dehydration. Call your doctor if bowel movements are frequent or unusually loose. Don't use any medication without consulting your doctor. Diarrhea in infants can be a very serious matter.

COLIC

The only nice thing to be said about colic is that it's usually gone after the first three months. The words "colic" and "colicky" are used often, but very few people know exactly what colic is.

Colic is severe pain in the intestine caused by the presence of undigested food; the baby's distress is essentially a symptom of indigestion. Colic is compounded by constipation, which is occasionally the sole cause of colic. The pain is the result of muscular spasms of the intestine.

It is hard to distinguish the cry of colic from the cry of hunger. Infants suffering from colic will usually take food eagerly and will be temporarily relieved of their discomfort after they eat. However, the pain soon returns, and there may be very few hours during a 24-hour period when the baby seems completely comfortable. Some babies suffer from colic on a very regular schedule—perhaps after the 2 p.m. or 6 p.m. feeding—and will cry violently for two hours or so. The only word of encouragement I can give you is that babies who suffer from colic are usually good weight-gainers. So don't despair.

Though milk may aggravate colic symptoms, in most cases it is not the cause. This is the reason your doctor may not change a colicky baby's formula immediately. Colic is thought to be caused by the immaturity of his digestive system, which allows inadequately digested food to enter the baby's intestinal tract. No matter how you are feeding—breast or bottle—the result will be the same. Keep in touch with your doctor. He can give you knowledgeable tips on how to cope with your baby, and he may have a few for *you,* just when you think you can't make it through another day.

✧◇◇

CELIAC DISEASE

✧◇◇

Celiac disease is a chronic digestive problem in which the most significant symptom is diarrhea containing undigested food, often frothy and extremely offensive. From time to time, mucus is passed. Your doctor's plan of treatment must be carried out faithfully. Recovery may be very slow, but there can be no lapse in discipline. The essential part of treatment is diet, because the disease is caused by the inability of the intestine to handle fats and starches. You will undoubtedly be advised to prepare a menu consisting mainly of protein foods from which gluten and fats have been eliminated. Doctors often advise giving the child skim milk, buttermilk, cottage cheese, and a little banana. Other foods are added slowly as the condition improves. Each additional food is an experiment, so the changes proceed slowly. Be prepared to be patient—it may be months or even years before a normal diet can be given. Your doctor will work closely with you and can best judge when your baby is ready for additional foods.

◇◈◇

CONSTIPATION

◇◈◇

Constipation isn't usually a serious problem with babies. It is not very common with breast feeding, and since it is slightly more prevalent with bottle feeding, formulas are made with different sugars, some more laxative than others.

If your baby isn't actually constipated but has hard, dry stools, it may help to add more liquid or fruit to his diet. Fruits, especially prunes, can help soften his bowel movements. During his first two or three months he may strain a lot when moving his bowels, but that doesn't necessarily mean that he is constipated. It takes a while for the anal opening to stretch. You can make him more comfortable by placing him on his back and holding his feet in the palm of your hand. This will give him something to push against. But an extremely stubborn case of constipation must be cared for by your doctor. Never give your baby a laxative or an enema without consulting the doctor first.

Above all, if your baby becomes ill, give him extra care, day and night. If he has a fever, sponge him with cool water, give him fruit juices, or just hold and rock him for a while. Give him all the love and attention you can; the household chores will wait. You won't spoil him, and when he's well again, he'll go back happily to his own activities.

Food Values

Your baby is remarkably busy during the first months of his life. He works so hard sucking his bottle that he often perspires while feeding. Then he waves his arms and legs, manages to creep around his crib, learns to hold his head up, and begins to turn over. Despite all this physical activity, he will probably double his birth weight by his fifth or sixth month. These accomplishments require enormous amounts of energy. All of this energy is provided by the body-building materials he eats. So before you start to prepare your baby's food, let's talk about different foods, their nutritional values, and what they mean to health.

vitamins

Vitamins are catalysts. Without them the food we eat would be insufficient for good health. They are needed in very small quantities, to ensure proper nutrition and growth and to keep every part of the body in good working condition.

Vitamin A is needed for healthy skin and eyes. A deficiency could make the skin dry, with an all-over goose-bump look, on baby's arms, bottom and thighs. This is also the vitamin that is necessary for keeping the internal linings of the body in good repair. Even though vitamin A can be stored in the body, it is still a good idea to eat daily the foods that provide it so that your body's supply doesn't run down. Babies get vitamin A from whole or fortified milk and, later, from liver, all the yellow vegetables, spinach and other green leafy vegetables, and eggs. Since many people are now using margarine in place of butter, many margarines are fortified with vitamin A. Carrots are a great source of vitamin A, the vitamin that helps us see at night.

Vitamin B is actually a group of many different vitamins. Therefore it is usually called vitamin B complex, and either the numbers (vitamin B_1, etc.) or the chemical names are used to tell them apart. *Thiamine* (B_1) stimulates appetite and growth, and also helps the body metabolize starches. When a baby starts to eat cereals, this last

function is very important. A deficiency of B_1 can work havoc with the nervous system, so if your baby is irritable, with a perpetual frown lining his face, check to see that you're feeding him enough sources of thiamine. He'll get it from his milk and, later, from liver, oranges, green vegetables, oatmeal, and whole-wheat or enriched cereals—and don't overlook the sweet potato. Ham, Canadian bacon and other forms of pork are among the best sources, so keep them in mind as soon as the baby is old enough to eat these foods.

Riboflavin (B$_2$) is important for growth and healthy skin. Lack of it causes cracks in the sides of the mouth, dry lips, and irritated eyes. To prevent all of these, it is important that a baby have, as soon as he's old enough, eggs, squash, beef, green peas and beans, poultry, and especially liver in addition to his milk, which is itself a very good source of riboflavin.

Pyridoxine (B$_6$) is necessary for the formation of red blood cells and hemoglobin, the substance that carries oxygen to all parts of the body. This vitamin also promotes healthy skin—one more reason why liver and other meats, eggs, and milk are so important.

A deficiency of *niacin,* another skin vitamin, causes pellagra, a serious disease marked by a blotchy red, extremely sore skin rash and chronic digestive troubles. Pellagra still exists in certain regions of the country where children are not given sufficient amounts of meat, poultry, fish, whole-wheat and enriched cereals and milk. Niacin transforms "energy" foods into energy for the body's use.

Cobalamine (B$_{12}$) is a blood vitamin that is not found in fruits or vegetables. Milk, eggs, cheese, and liver and other meats are the main sources. Cobalamine is used to treat pernicious anemia.

Though a baby is not likely to get scurvy nowadays, a shortage of vitamin C (ascorbic acid) could be responsible for susceptibility to colds and a tendency to suffer from black-and-blue bruises, and gum problems. Vitamin C cannot be stored in the body, so it's very important that your baby get orange juice or tomato juice and a leafy green vegetable every day. Heat destroys vitamin C, so don't warm orange juice for your baby; room temperature is just fine. Other sources of ascorbic acid are cantaloupe, strawberries, sweet and white potatoes, and beef liver.

Vitamin D is important for teeth and bones, and is often called the sunshine vitamin because ultraviolet rays produce vitamin D in the skin. It is found in milk that has been fortified, fish-liver oils (remember those long winter months laced with cod-liver oil?), butter, liver, fish, and eggs. The most important function of vitamin D is to help the body absorb calcium and phosphorus, two minerals essential for sturdy bones and teeth.

Vitamin E is important for healthy skin and is found in soybeans, other legumes, green leafy vegetables, wheat germ, whole-grain cereals, and our faithful friends milk, eggs, butter and liver.

Vitamin K helps the blood to clot. Spinach and other green leafy vegetables, egg yolk, liver, and tomatoes are among the best sources of this vitamin.

Most doctors routinely prescribe multivitamin drops containing vitamins A, C, and D. The drops, together with a balanced diet, will almost guarantee a happy, healthy baby. You will be surprised at how the baby loves this "medicine."

I always feel a little lost when I read that such and such a vitamin is present in green leafy vegetables or yellow vegetables or fruits, but see no mention of specific foods. So I made myself a list of the vitamins and the most important food sources for each one.

Vitamin A	Beef liver, fish (such as halibut), apricots, peaches, squash, sweet potatoes, spinach, broccoli, carrots, eggs, butter, cheese, fortified margarine
Vitamin B Thiamine (B$_1$)	Pork, liver, lima beans, green peas, sweet and white potatoes, precooked cereals, wheat germ, farina, oranges, milk
Riboflavin (B$_2$)	Lamb, liver, beef, pork, poultry, fish (such as salmon), squash, green peas and beans, milk, precooked cereals, eggs, cheese
Pyridoxine (B$_6$)	Liver, meats, eggs, cheese, milk
Cobalamine (B$_{12}$)	Meat, milk, eggs, liver, cheese
Niacin	Liver, eggs, veal, fish (such as halibut and salmon), poultry, whole-wheat and enriched cereals, milk
Vitamin C	Orange juice, grapefruit juice, tomatoes, green leafy vegetables, sweet and white potatoes, strawberries, cantaloupe, beef liver
Vitamin D	Sunshine, fish-liver oil, fish, liver, eggs, butter, fortified milk
Vitamin E	Wheat germ, soybeans, green leafy vegetables, whole-grain cereals, milk, eggs, butter, liver
Vitamin K	Spinach, tomatoes, egg yolks, liver

minerals

Minerals also perform important functions in the body. Bones and teeth are hardened by calcium and phosphorus and the body depends on sodium and potassium to help maintain the body's fluid balance. Iodine contributes to a good circulatory system, important for healthy skin and shiny hair. Iron supplies pep and gives the blush to baby's lips and cheeks. Iron is also part of the blood element, hemoglobin, that carries oxygen to all parts of the body; and it is vital for the production of new red blood cells.

Good sources of iron are liver, spinach, and egg yolk; calcium and phosphorus are plentiful in milk and cheese. Seafood is rich in iodine, and an extra measure can be found in iodized table salt.

Most foods contain a variety of minerals, but they will be lost if you overcook in large quantities of water.

protein

If there is any one thing that you could say the body is made of, it would be protein. The heart, brain, muscle, nerves, and lungs are made up largely of protein. Even bones contain protein with calcium and phosphorus added to make them hard. Without sufficient protein a baby will not have good muscle tone, he may become more susceptible to infections and anemia, and scratches will not heal as quickly as they should. Because a baby is constantly growing he needs a great deal of protein to increase every part of his body, inside and out. Since protein can't be stored in the body, the baby requires, besides his milk, some meat, poultry, eggs, cheese, or fish daily as soon as these foods can be given to him.

Other sources of protein are whole-grain cereals and such vegetables as soybeans and dried white beans, lentils, and chickpeas. But these do not contain all the necessary protein elements and should only supplement the "complete" protein foods, such as meat and eggs—they cannot be substituted for them.

fats and carbohydrates

Fats and carbohydrates—sugars and starches—are energy foods. They provide the fuel that the baby needs for his daily activities. His little body needs this concentrated energy to keep up with his rapid growth, and he'll need even larger amounts of carbohydrates and fats when he starts to toddle around the house. Fats are also necessary to maintain healthy skin and protect muscles and nerves. They are also a source of vitamins.

Your baby will amaze you with his energy. Always looking, reaching, touching, pulling, moving—every day brings something new. It's exhausting just to watch him. Make sure his diet has plenty of milk and, later on, cheese to provide fats, along with sugar, honey, cereals, potatoes, and other starchy vegetables, bread, and noodles to give him the necessary carbohydrates.

water

Water plays a very important part in the make-up of your baby's body. He seems so soft and fluid, and indeed he should, because his body actually consists of 60 to 70 percent water. The passing of large amounts of urine is one of the conditions of infancy, and sufficient water must be given him to make this possible. Your baby will get most of his daily fluids from his milk, and also from the food he will eat, but give him a few drinks of water during the day from a bottle—especially on hot days when he is perspiring.

roughage

Roughage is the cellulose, or fiber, in vegetables, fruits, and grains. It adds bulk in the intestine to stimulate bowel movements. Cellulose is not digested or absorbed, and has no nutritional value, but if it is not included in the baby's diet he may become constipated.

calories

There is a great deal of talk about calories from time to time, and somehow we've come to think of "calories" as meaning the difference between fat and skinny. Well, forget that! When we discuss the caloric content of food, we are talking about the fuel or energy value that different foods contain and make available to the body. The calorie is just the unit of measurement.

During his first year, the baby needs about 50 calories per pound of body weight every twenty-four hours. This is almost twice the amount proportionately required by an adult. The baby's food must supply enough energy for his daily activities, maintain his body temperature, and also give him the extra fuel he requires for growing. When a baby (or a grownup, for that matter!) eats more than his body needs, the excess calories turn into fat. I surely don't advocate

48

overly fat babies, but a little extra fatty tissue not only keeps him warm, but can be used on days when he needs the reserve fuel.

Fats contain twice as many calories as an equal weight of sugar, starch, or protein. Butter, cream, and oils are very high in calories because they are rich in fat.

Meat, fish, eggs, and cheese contain both fat and protein, and are an excellent source of fuel and energy. Vegetables are divided into three groups when we are counting calories. Starchy vegetables, such as potatoes (both white and sweet), lima beans, and corn, are highest in calories. The middle category includes beets, peas, onions, and winter squash. Vegetables that are low or very low in calories include lettuce, celery, carrots, summer squash, string beans, cabbage, spinach, tomatoes, asparagus , broccoli, and cauliflower.

Most fruits are moderate in calorie content unless sugar is added to them.

Cereals, breads, and noodles, which contain large amounts of starch, are all very high in calories. Starches are carbohydrates, and all carbohydrates have high caloric value.

Milk is a combination of natural sugar, protein, and fat, and is another great source of calories for energy. Caloric values of the various forms of milk depend on their fat content.

Now that we have discussed all the nutrients that provide a balanced diet, it may seem complicated and exasperating to get one small baby to consume everything he needs. Up until this time, his meals supplement the nutrients in his formula or milk. Here is a basic food-planning guide with the constituents and quantities that a child should have daily after the age of six months.

❖❖❖

Milk: 1½ pints, including the milk used in cooking his meals

Juice: 3 ounces

Meat or poultry: 1 ounce or more

Fish (after ten months) : 1 ounce or more, as a substitute for meat or poultry

Egg: 1 (an egg can be substituted occasionally for meat or poultry)

Vegetables: 3–5 ounces, once or twice a day

Starch: 2 ounces of potatoes or lima beans, or any other starchy vegetable

Fats: ½ ounce of butter or margarine, or cod-liver oil if the doctor prescribes it

Whole-grain cereals or bread: twice a day

Fruit: once or twice a day

A typical daily menu that would satisfy these nutritional requirements would be:

Breakfast	Fruit juice
	Cereal *or* enriched bread
	Egg
	Milk
Lunch	Meat *or* poultry *or* fish
	Vegetable
	Starchy vegetable
	Fruit
	Milk
Dinner	Cereal *or* soup *or* macaroni *or* egg with enriched bread
	Vegetable
	Fruit
	Milk

❖❖

Since your mind is bogged down with technicalities right now, I won't bother you with more, but make a mental note that if you need to know "what equals what"—how much juice an orange makes, or how many tablespoons are in an ounce—there's a chart on page 145.

Kitchen Equipment

Now that there's a baby in the house, there may be a few pieces of kitchen equipment that you'll need to buy. You probably have most of the items on the following list, which contains all of the essential equipment for preparing the recipes in this book.

Don't be gadget-happy and buy all sorts of wonder tools that are supposed to chop, shred, slice, blend, crush, peel, and vacuum the floors, all at the same time. They often create more problems than they solve. Make sure that any time-saving utensil you purchase does just that—saves time. For instance, a good-quality swivel-bladed vegetable peeler that will both peel and cut thin slices, and a good-quality rubber spatula that will follow the contours of your blender container, will save you a considerable amount of irritation as well as time. If you have a discount store nearby, do your shopping there. The quality will be the same if you stick to brand names, and the money you save will be appreciable.

❖❖❖❖❖❖❖❖❖❖❖❖❖❖❖❖❖❖❖❖❖❖❖❖❖❖❖❖❖❖❖❖❖❖❖❖❖❖❖

BLENDER

❖❖❖❖❖❖❖❖❖❖❖❖❖❖❖❖❖❖❖❖❖❖❖❖❖❖❖❖❖❖❖❖❖❖❖❖❖❖❖

Without a blender it is much more difficult to achieve the puréed consistency—the perfect smoothness—that the baby's first meals require. The blender is your most essential appliance, and it is also the most expensive item on the list. Shop carefully and compare styles and prices. Or, when a favorite aunt, or a group of your friends ask what "big" thing you want, after you've got your crib and carriage, suggest this useful appliance.

If you're only likely to use your blender for preparing your baby's food, a model with two speeds is just as efficient as one with several speeds. Of course, once you have a blender you'll find that you can use it to make failure-proof hollandaise sauce, chop onions (you can save all your tears for the late movie), and make fabulous potato-pancake batter. You'll never grate again!

A blender is a tool designed to make your work easier. If you enjoy cooking and relish the idea (no pun intended) of a complicated sauce or dessert, select a blender with the widest range of speeds and actions. If not, one that simply turns on and off will be fine.

When you start puréeing small quantities of baby food in your blender, you may find that the food swirls to the sides of the container and will not fall back to the blades. If this happens, take the removable center piece out of the lid; or, if your blender doesn't have a center piece, leave the top loose and slightly off to one side. This eliminates the partial vacuum by letting in additional air, and the food will stay around the blades. Don't worry about splashing over—there's no danger of this when you are blending a small amount of food.

One note of caution: most manufacturers do not recommend the use of a dishwasher for washing the blender container, so read your instruction booklet carefully and follow its directions for washing and maintenance.

❖◇❖

SMALL PARING KNIFE

❖◇❖

Using a dull knife in the kitchen is like trying to trim your cuticle with the garden shears. A sharp paring knife is indispensable for small jobs of dicing and cutting vegetables, mincing parsley, and coring apples. Buy a good piece of cutlery and you'll pass it on to your daughter in twenty years.

RUBBER SPATULA

I always keep two rubber spatulas in my kitchen drawer. I have a large one for scraping mixing bowls and the blender container and a small one for scraping out small jars. Rubber spatulas are more flexible than plastic ones. Both types will last much longer if you take the time to wash and dry them by hand instead of putting them in the dishwasher.

SLOTTED SPOON

Using a slotted spoon is the easiest way to lift food from a saucepan and drain off the cooking liquid. You may have received a slotted spoon in a set of kitchen utensils as a wedding or shower gift. But if you have to buy your own, select a spoon with a heat-resistant handle.

MEASURING SPOONS

These are very inexpensive, and you'll find it convenient to have two sets handy. One set always seems to be wet just when you want to measure another tablespoon of flour. Remember to measure accurately at all times by leveling dry ingredients in the measuring spoon with the straight edge of a knife blade or metal spatula.

MEASURING CUPS

At the risk of giving the impression of duplicating equipment, I also recommend two measuring cups. The one-quart measuring cup is perfect for mixing the formula, but it is difficult to use when you're working with small quantities of food. A one-cup measuring cup is necessary for everyday cooking when you're measuring small quantities.

FOOD MILL

A food mill is nice to have for several baby-food recipes and for day-to-day cooking, but it is not essential. Borrow one from your mother, but don't buy one unless you really plan to use it. The food mill can be used for puréeing fruits and vegetables, but it is entirely unsuitable for puréeing meats. The blender will purée fruits, vegetables, *and* meats, and will do a better job on all foods except potatoes. In the preparation of mashed potatoes and potato soup, the food mill is unsurpassed for retaining a pleasant texture.

Another feature of the food mill is the manner in which it will purée fruit and remove the skins, cores, and seeds at the same time. Apples, peaches, plums, apricots, and pears can be cooked with their skins intact. When they are put through the food mill, the skins, core, and seeds will remain in the basket.

There are food mills that have interchangeable plates that give various degrees of fineness; others have a single fixed blade.

The electric blender has replaced the food mill for many jobs, but before the blender came along, anything that had to be puréed was done with the food mill or, even more laboriously, with a sieve and spoon. The choice of having another masher around the house is up to you and your husband.

MEAT GRINDER

A good old-fashioned meat grinder will give you the perfect consistency for junior foods—somewhere between the smooth purée for infants and the finely chopped texture for two-year-olds. A meat grinder is another item that you should try to borrow rather than buy, since its usefulness after the baby is older may be limited. It's also possible to buy electric mixers with a meat-grinding attachment.

If you decide to buy a conventional meat grinder, you'll find that its appearance is as old-fashioned as the principle on which it operates. It's still a clumsy-looking old thing that clamps onto the edge of your counter. If your counter tops have no overhang, look for a grinder with a suction-cup base.

VEGETABLE PEELER

There are many different types of vegetable peelers on the market, but the best of the lot is still the original swivel-bladed peeler, more commonly known as a potato peeler. It's been through two world wars and a number of police actions, and it will quickly become the hero of your kitchen. It has an easy-to-grip handle, a long, double-edged swivel blade, and sometimes a little gadget on the end of the handle that I've never used, but which is designed for cutting beans French style.

TONGS

About thirty seconds after the discovery of fire, someone invented tongs. Today, they are indispensable for removing the baby's bottles, nipples, and caps from the sterilizer, so I have listed them with the formula-making equipment. But even after your sterilizing days are over, tongs will remain one of your most prized kitchen tools for an endless variety of jobs—for turning steaks without piercing the meat, or for retrieving corn on the cob or lobster from a pot of boiling water.

WIRE-MESH STRAINERS

Two different-sized strainers are a good investment for any well-equipped kitchen. Choose a small-size strainer that will fit snugly into a water glass for straining the pulp from orange juice. Your larger strainer should have hooks on one side of the basket (for hooking over the edge of a pot or mixing bowl) and a long handle. This large sieve will be used mainly for straining soups and draining large quantities of vegetables.

57

GRATER

The best grater to own, in my opinion, is the type that is usually called a potato grater. It has a large, flat grating surface, about five by nine inches, made of crinkly wires attached to a metal frame and handle.

VEGETABLE BRUSH

Vegetables have usually been rinsed before they are delivered to your greengrocer or supermarket, but there will always be some garden soil remaining. And within that soil there may be traces of pesticides. All vegetables must be scrubbed with a stiff-bristled vegetable brush before they are prepared for the baby, even if they are to be peeled. This rule applies to fruits as well, but be more gentle with them.

DOUBLE BOILER

Preparing your baby's food in a double boiler is the best way to avoid burning or scorching it. It takes longer to cook food in a double boiler than over a direct flame, but it's less hazardous. A double boiler is also convenient for keeping cooked cereal warm and smooth if you want to prepare breakfast before the baby wakes.

The glass double boilers are breakable and may need a little more care than the metal ones. The advantage of the glass kind is that you can keep your eye on the water level as you cook.

⊗◇
ENAMEL SAUCEPAN
⊗◇

This little pot, listed for formula-making, too, is worth its weight in gold. Whenever you have to boil water, use an enamel saucepan. Because it won't discolor, it will save you hours of scouring. Use it for poaching eggs, cooking vegetables, and heating your baby's bottles. Buy it a lid and it will become the prince among pots in your kitchen.

⊗◇
FRUIT JUICER
⊗◇

For squeezing orange, grapefruit, and lemon juice in quantities for the baby, a small plastic juicer (with a strainer for removing the pulp and seeds, and a bottom cup for collecting the juice) is fine.

⊗◇
HEAVY ALUMINUM SAUCEPAN
⊗◇

A heavy one-and-a-half-quart aluminum saucepan is a boon to any kitchen. It is marvelous for making sauces and custards, and for browning meats. Water should not be boiled in an aluminum pan because it will discolor the metal.

STAINLESS-STEEL SAUCEPAN

A one-and-a-half-quart stainless-steel saucepan is handy for preparing stews and casseroles. Stainless steel is easy to clean, although it isn't as satisfactory for browning meats and preparing sauces as an aluminum saucepan.

CHEESECLOTH

A package of cheesecloth is always handy to have around the house, and the arrival of your baby will increase its usefulness. Make small bags out of cheesecloth and string and use them to keep baby's spoons, nipples, and caps together in the dishwasher and sterilizer. Cheesecloth also makes a suitable strainer for soups if your metal sieves are not clean or are out of reach. Then, when you're finished with the kitchen, you could think about cheesecloth for cleaning, waxing, polishing, or antiquing the baby's furniture.

ALUMINUM FOIL, PLASTIC WRAP, AND WAXED PAPER

Keep a roll of each of these handy. Use the plastic for covering the unused portion of canned formula before refrigerating it. Use the foil or plastic for covering dishes of leftovers, and use either heavy-weight foil or freezer-weight plastic for packaging food for the freezer.

Guess Who's Coming for Dinner

Before you start scrubbing potatoes and scrambling eggs, let's talk about the general preparation and serving of foods for your baby.

All the recipes in this book can be, and are meant to be, prepared while you are cooking your family's daily meals. If you are making cereal cooked with milk for breakfast, add half a cup of milk and one and a half tablespoons of cereal to your usual amounts. This will make just enough extra for the baby. If you have to bake a cake for the hospital bazaar, use the oven time to make a pudding or custard for the baby. And the next time you make spaghetti sauce, save out some ingredients and simmer a meatball soup with vegetables on the side.

If you work efficiently in the kitchen, preparing your baby's food will take very little extra effort and no extra time. In fact, many times the meat and vegetables that you serve for dinner can be shared with your baby without any additional preparation other than puréeing in your blender. For instance, if you are planning to have broiled steak, purée a small part of the lean meat with fat-free meat juices from the broiler pan; purée whatever vegetable you are having (following the recipes in this book) and serve it to the baby with fruit or a light dessert, and top off with a bottle.

When holidays roll around, take a few slices of roast turkey or roast beef, add a little fat-free natural gravy and a couple of tablespoons of vegetable cooking liquid, purée them in your blender, and your baby can celebrate with the rest of the family. (There are specific quantities and instructions for each of these meals in the recipe section.)

The amount of food that each recipe yields is measured in cups or fractions of cups. Appetites vary from baby to baby. In fact, a baby's appetite will vary from day to day. It's quite possible that half a cup of food will be a single serving for a four-month-old sixteen-pound baby, but the same quantity will yield two servings for a five-month-old thirteen-pound baby. Even babies that are the same weight and age may have entirely different appetites. Don't become upset if your baby's appetite fluctuates. The meals that you will serve him will be tasty and nourishing, so rest assured that he'll eat what his appetite demands on that particular day.

Storing Food

It's important to remember, if you want to save what's left in the baby's dish, that the bacteria in saliva will cause food to spoil rapidly. If you're working with large quantities of food, always transfer a small amount from the blender to the baby's dish. Then you can spoon-feed your baby from the dish with no danger of saliva being introduced into the unused portion. It's easy enough to refill the baby's dish if he is still hungry, but always remember to use a spoon in the untouched food that's different from the one you are feeding with. Any uneaten food left in the baby's dish must be thrown away.

The food remaining in your blender should be refrigerated immediately in a clean storage dish, and used the following day. If you're not planning to use it the next day, or if you have prepared enough for several servings, it must be frozen. Any baby food that has been in the refrigerator for more than two days should be discarded. Don't take any chances with spoilage when your baby's health is in question.

As you become proficient in preparing puréed foods for your baby, double or triple the recipes. Then freeze the extra servings immediately after cooking, just as you would freeze casserole meals for the family. On busy days you'll have the convenience of pre-cooked baby foods whose ingredients and preparation you have controlled.

After a thorough washing, the containers that were used for individual servings of yogurt and ice cream make excellent freezer containers. You can also buy small, inexpensive plastic cups with tight-fitting lids that hold exactly half a cup of baby food. Always label and date baby-food containers before you freeze them, to avoid confusion two weeks later. It is difficult to identify unmarked containers, and almost impossible to remember how long they've been there.

The Taste of Food

The very first time you sit down and feed your baby from a dish, you are beginning to mold his eating patterns for a lifetime. The sense of taste functions at birth and develops rapidly. Introduce as many different tastes and textures into the baby's diet as you can before he reaches the "age of objection." This is the period, at about eight or nine months of age, when your baby will inevitably begin to express his likes and dislikes about everything—the bath he has to endure, the naps he thinks unnecessary, and the food he doesn't have time for. This is the age at which grandparents remark, "My, he certainly has a mind of his own."

If your baby experiences a variety of tastes within his first year, he will be more likely to try new foods as he grows older. I'm not saying that he must become a gourmet, but that he can have the greater satisfaction that comes with experiencing a variety of foods rather than just eating the same old "meat and potatoes."

Of course, there will be certain foods that the baby will dislike, and which you'll feel he must have for proper nutrition. But don't force him to eat if he consistently objects to a food. As long as he is eating a balanced diet of foods that he *does* like, provide substitutes and permit him to be selective. This really isn't being "permissive," but is being sensible by avoiding a hassle over something that isn't important. What *is* important, aside from nutritional requirements, is the influence that you bring to bear on eating habits and behavior.

Your baby's eating habits as well as his general behavior will be affected by the way you handle mealtimes. If you are tense and anxious, the baby will soon sense this and react with fretfulness. Then, as you urge him to eat, he will balk. Avoid this simply by relaxing. Mealtime is a pleasant time for you to sit down and enjoy your baby's company. At the same time, keep a cheerful but firm hand on the situation. When your baby loses interest in what he's eating, chances are he's full. If he wants to get out of his chair to play or crawl, don't traipse around the house behind him, spoon and plate in hand, coaxing him to eat. Once he feels that he can dominate the situation, and senses your frustration, you have completely lost control. Instead, end the mealtime quietly and let the baby go on to his next activity. Be prepared and willing to feed him his next meal a bit earlier if necessary. When a child is really hungry, he'll sit very attentively and eat like a trooper.

Watching Him Grow

Observing your new baby during his first few weeks will leave you a bit awestruck. You will spend countless hours fascinated by his movements and his growing awareness, and the perfecting of his miniature features. As the weeks go by, you'll wonder if he's capable of thinking or even what he's thinking, and you will be amazed at the progress of his physical development.

His progress in motor skills—head turning, rolling over, sitting up, and crawling—is obvious, and these are delightful adventures to observe. Mental development is not as easy to perceive. Although the very young baby watches your movements intently, and you know he's aware of you, it's difficult to communicate with him. Later on, when his physical and mental actions begin to coordinate, and he looks up and smiles at you when you enter the room, you will truly know you're dealing with a miniature human being. You will spend every free moment observing his actions, and at the same time he will be watching you in order to learn.

For the first three or four months, your baby doesn't really know what food is, or what happens to it when you bring the spoon close to him. He eats instinctively, and as he grows older he enjoys watching you eat. He watches, he mimics, he associates, and he learns. Eventually he will recognize that the milk you drink from a glass is the same as the milk that he drinks from a bottle. If you give him a sip from time to time, even though it will certainly dribble down his front, he'll make the connection quicker. Since, when you cook it yourself, some of his food is a puréed version of yours, there will be foods that he can sample from your dish—such as creamed spinach, mashed potatoes, or applesauce. He'll watch you thrust food into an opening in your face, and he'll soon learn that he, too, must have an opening and that his own mouth is where the food is going.

After that, unfortunately, everything from paper to powder puffs goes into his mouth for tasting. You'll have to watch him every minute until he's beyond that discovery. But you can also look forward to the day when he'll pass by a mirror and a spark of recognition will flash across his face—and a squeal of joy will announce the emergence of another social being.

Cooking for Baby

Your Baby's First Solid Foods

(AT FOUR TO SIX WEEKS)

CEREAL

When he's about four to six weeks old your baby will get his first solid food, and that will be cereal. Because it is smooth and has been prepared with that good familiar milk or formula, cereal is the easiest transition food from bottle to spoon.

Cereal can be prepared with either milk or formula, and your doctor will tell you which he prefers. Some doctors will suggest that you continue using formula to avoid the risk of upsetting your baby's digestive system. Others feel that a few ounces of milk used in the cereal will give a good indication of how the baby will take the change-over from formula to milk within the following month or two.

The best times of the day to feed your baby cereal are ten o'clock in the morning and six o'clock in the evening. The evening feeding of cereal which fills his tummy and staves off hunger may be the little push he needs to sleep through the night.

The first few attempts at feeding him with a spoon will make you giggle. Cover yourself and the baby and get ready for a mess. Hold

70

your baby in a slightly more upright position than you would if you were giving him a bottle or breast feeding. Again, if you are relaxed with him, he'll hardly know that he's being introduced to something new. If he does protest these first attempts at eating from a spoon, try again a few days later. All you are interested in at this point is getting him used to the spoon; he's still getting ample nourishment from his formula. If you are too pushy, he may just turn down the whole idea of being spoon-fed. If you feed him some milk first, he will fill up his tummy and be more patient throughout this adventure.

Don't be discouraged when most of the cereal dribbles down his chin the first few times. Until this point he has gotten all his food by sucking. He's still sucking now, but it isn't working out too well since this pushes the cereal upward and out of his mouth. Don't worry. Miraculously, he'll very quickly get the idea of eating.

If he really wrinkles up his face at the new adventure, be a little sneaky and try a little fruit, such as puréed apples or pears mixed in with the cereal to make it a bit sweeter. A small sprinkle of sugar, a few drops of honey, or the tiniest slice of butter or margarine can also add that little something extra to make his cereal tastier. However, don't oversweeten in your enthusiasm to make your baby like his cereal. Remember that honey is a natural sweetener, and preferable to sugar.

There is disagreement concerning butter in a baby's diet because butter is a milk-fat product and contains cholesterol. Although butter does have flavor value and the nutritional element of vitamin A, it isn't advisable to use it in great quantities. I personally don't think an occasional bit of butter is harmful, but if you have any doubts at all, check with your physician.

❖◇

PRECOOKED CEREALS

❖◇

Precooked cereals that are specially prepared for babies have been treated by a high-heat process that changes part of the starch to sugar and makes them very easy for the baby to digest. Since these cereals require no cooking, all you have to do is add enough warm milk or formula to achieve the proper consistency.

Precooked cereals can be purchased in variety packs of different grains—wheat, barley, oats, and rice—and soybeans. Soybean cereal is high in vegetable protein and iron. Although rice cereal contains more starch than any of the others, it is usually the first cereal that babies are given because it seems to be the easiest to digest.

First Cereal Feedings

1 tablespoon dry, precooked cereal
5 tablespoons warm milk *or* formula
Honey (optional)
Pour milk or formula into a small bowl. Stir in the cereal with a teaspoon. *Yields ¼ cup.*

This proportion of milk to cereal will make a very thin consistency, not much thicker than the formula itself. When your baby becomes accustomed to spoon feeding, increase the amount of cereal to 2 tablespoons and decrease the liquid to 3 tablespoons to make a thicker consistency. Precooked cereals tend to be pasty, so it helps to add a tablespoon or two of extra milk or formula, pouring it around the edge of the bowl. Scoop a little of it up with each spoonful of cereal. A drop or two of honey is a good natural sweetener and has a slight laxative effect.

❖◇

CEREALS FOR YOU TO COOK

❖◇

When my baby was about a month old, I found that she preferred homemade cereal to precooked cereal. Its creamier texture prevented it from getting stuck to the roof of her mouth. On cold winter days, I simply increased the recipe for the baby's cereal made with milk and cooked enough for the entire family.

Of course, all cereals should be cooled to a safe serving temperature before feeding the baby; test the cereal before offering it.

Cream of Wheat, or Farina

1/2 cup milk *or* formula
1 1/2 tablespoons cream of wheat or other enriched farina
Sugar *or* honey (optional)

Heat milk or formula in a small pan until it starts to bubble around the edges. Sprinkle in the farina and cook for 5 minutes, stirring until thickened.

Spoon into serving bowl and allow to sit at room temperature for several minutes. Add a tablespoon or two of cold milk to cool it further, if necessary.

Sprinkle lightly with sugar or add a drop or two of honey. Yields 1/3 cup.

Variation: For a slightly creamier version, use a double boiler. Cook as directed above for 2 minutes in the top section of the boiler, set over direct heat. Then place over boiling water in the bottom section, cover and cook, stirring occasionally, for 5 or 6 minutes until smooth and creamy.

The double boiler is also great if you want to make the cereal ahead of time and warm it just before serving. However, it should be made within an hour of serving to prevent spoiling.

Oatmeal

1 cup water
1/2 cup quick-cooking oatmeal
Milk
1/2 teaspoon butter (optional)
Sugar *or* honey (optional)

Mix water and oatmeal in a small saucepan. Bring to a boil and cook for 2 minutes over medium heat, stirring frequently. Remove from heat, cover, and let stand for 5 minutes.

Spoon into a small bowl and stir in the butter, if used. Pour on a little cold milk and sprinkle with sugar or honey, if you like. Yields 1/2 cup.

Cream of Rice

2/3 cup milk *or* formula
2 tablespoons Cream of Rice
1/2 teaspoon butter (optional)
Milk

Heat milk or formula in a small saucepan until bubbles appear around the edges. Sprinkle in Cream of Rice very slowly, stirring constantly for 2 minutes. Cover and cook over low heat for 4 minutes more. Spoon cereal into a small bowl. Stir in butter, if you like, and pour on a little cold milk. Yields 1/2 cup.

fruits

Fruits are what most babies like best. They are usually added to the diet at the same time as cereal, and are fed to the baby with his cereal at the 10 a.m. and 6 p.m. feedings. Most fruits are so naturally sweet and smooth that they can be used to camouflage some of the things the baby doesn't like. It sounds like a terrible thing to do, but there will be times when you may have to give him crushed aspirin or some other medication with a disagreeable taste—babies are so enthusiastic about fruit that they will gobble it down.

Try a new fruit for at least five days before you add another one, and start by giving the baby a small taste. Some babies will be allergic to a particular fruit. If your baby develops a rash, or soreness in the diaper area, eliminate the new fruit from his diet for a month or so. This one-at-a-time method will save you a lot of detective work.

Ripe banana is the only fruit your baby should eat raw at first. All others must be cooked until he is at least eight months old. The mildest to start off with are applesauce, bananas, and pears. Later you can add plums, peaches, and apricots. Two tablespoons are plenty at first.

Most of the following recipes call for the use of a blender. If you don't have a blender at this time, a food mill will suffice, but the consistency of the purée will not be as smooth. As I mentioned earlier, if you have trouble puréeing small quantities of fruit in your blender, take the removable center piece out of the lid, or if your blender doesn't have a center piece, leave the top loose and set it off a bit to one side.

Pour the puréed fruit into small containers with tight-fitting lids and refrigerate. Puréed fruits can be stored for three to four days in the refrigerator. Serve the fruit at room temperature during the baby's first few months. But as the baby gets older he may enjoy his fruit chilled.

74

Bananas

1 medium banana, fully ripe and speckled

Cut the banana in half and then peel it. Mash one half with a fork. The consistency of the mashed banana will be right without any added liquid.

Cover the remaining half with plastic wrap, refrigerate it, and use it the following day. Yields about ½ cup.

Pears

1 ripe pear
1 tablespoon water

Wash the pear, peel and core it. Cut the entire pear into small pieces, making sure that all seeds are removed. Put the pieces into a small saucepan with a lid. Add the water and simmer for 5 minutes. Drain well. Purée cooked pear in a blender.

If you are puréeing the pear in a food mill, do not peel or core it. Cut the pear into small pieces and cook. The food mill will remove the skins, core, and seeds as the pear is being puréed. Yields ½ cup.

Applesauce

To make applesauce, use any good all-purpose apple (not the green ones), such as Cortland, McIntosh, or Winesap. Though Golden Delicious is an eating apple, it makes the best applesauce you have ever tasted.

You will notice that the apple skins are included in the recipe. The skins add color and flavor and also have vitamins and minerals stored in them. Because you are using the skins, the apples should be washed especially carefully.

2 medium apples
1 tablespoon sugar
⅓ cup water
1 teaspoon lemon juice (optional)

Wash apples very well. Peel, saving the skins, and core. Cut the apples into small pieces. Place in a saucepan, adding the skins at one side of the pot. Add sugar, water, and lemon juice. Cover and cook over medium heat for 12 minutes, or until apples are soft.

If you are puréeing the apples in a food mill, simply wash and cut them into small pieces before cooking. Add the other ingredients and cook until apples are soft. The skins, core, and seeds will remain in the basket as you purée the fruit.

Discard skins and any remaining cooking liquid. Purée in a blender for several seconds. Yields about 1 cup.

Peaches

Fresh peaches in season are delicious, and taste far superior to the strained peaches that come in a jar.

2 ripe peaches
1 tablespoon sugar
½ cup water

Wash the peaches and place them in a small saucepan. Cover with boiling water and let stand for a minute or two. The skins will now slip off the peaches very easily. (This method of peeling is called blanching.) Discard the water. It is not necessary to remove the peach skins if you are using a food mill to purée the fruit.

Cut peaches in half and remove pits. Put the fruit into a saucepan and add sugar and water. Cover and simmer for 10 minutes or until tender. Lift peaches out of the syrup with a slotted spoon and reserve the syrup. Purée peaches in your blender or food mill. The juice you have saved will add a nice flavor to baby's cereal and can be used instead of sugar. Yields about 1 cup.

Apricots

6 fully ripe apricots
3 tablespoons sugar
1/2 cup water

Wash apricots and place them in a small saucepan. Cover with boiling water and let stand for a minute or two. The skins will now slip off with ease. Discard the water. Don't remove the apricot skins if you are using a food mill to purée the fruit. The skins will remain in the basket.

Cut the apricots in half and remove the seeds. Place the apricots in a saucepan and add sugar and water. Cover and simmer for 12 minutes or until tender.

Lift apricots out of the syrup with a slotted spoon and reserve the syrup. Purée in a food mill or a blender. Use the reserved juice, if you like, on the baby's cereal. Yields about 1 cup.

Plums

The best plums for stewing are the small purple ones called prune plums or blue plums.

12 ripe prune plums
4 tablespoons sugar
1/2 cup water

Wash the plums well. Cut them in half and remove the seeds.

Place the plums, sugar, and water in a small saucepan. Cover and simmer slowly until tender, about 15 minutes.

Lift the plums out of the juice and cool. Reserve the syrup for plum pudding.

Purée in a blender or food mill. Don't bother to remove the skins if you use a food mill—the skins won't go through the sieve. If you are using a blender, remove the skins first; you'll do this best with your fingers. Plums vary in sweetness, so taste to find out if they need a bit more sugar. Yields about 1 1/2 cups.

Canned Plums

Canned purple plums make a delightful winter substitute for fresh plums. Drain the syrup from 1-pound can and save it for the next recipe (Plum Pudding). Remove the skins and seeds—this finger work tends to be a little messy. Blend for a few seconds, or purée in a food mill. Yields about ¾ cup.

Baby's Plum Pudding

This old Pennsylvania Dutch recipe was originally called Plum Mush. It can also be made with the syrup from cherries or peaches, and when the baby is older, with the syrup from stewed blueberries or blackberries. It can be eaten plain or spooned over boiled custard.

½ cup plus 1 tablespoon plum syrup
¼ teaspoon lemon juice
Tiny pinch of cinnamon
1½ teaspoons cornstarch

Mix ½ cup of the syrup, the lemon juice, and cinnamon in a small saucepan and bring to a boil.

In a small bowl, mix the remaining syrup into the cornstarch to make a smooth paste. Stir paste into the boiling syrup very slowly. Continue to stir until syrup begins to clear and thicken, about 2 minutes.

Remove from heat. The pudding will thicken as it cools. Yields ½ cup.

Puréed Prunes

12 dried prunes
Water
⅛ teaspoon vanilla

Place the prunes in a small saucepan and cover with water. Bring to a rapid boil, and then reduce the heat, cover, and simmer for 25 minutes.

Cool prunes, then drain off and reserve the juice. Remove the seeds from the prunes (using your fingers is easiest). Purée the prunes in a blender or food mill. Stir in vanilla.

The consistency should be slightly thicker than applesauce. If too thick, add 1 or 2 tablespoons of the reserved juice. Yields about 1 cup.

Vegetables and Meats

AT ABOUT THREE MONTHS

Sometime around the age of two and a half to three months, vegetables and meats are added to your baby's expanding diet.

All the following recipes have been thoroughly tested and given a hearty burp of approval by my own happy and healthy children. The procedures are easy to follow, and even the most inexperienced cook will have no difficulty.

No matter what food you are preparing, it must be puréed to a very smooth consistency—one similar to that of the cereal and fruits to which your baby has become accustomed.

vegetables

Vegetables, like fruits, should be added to your baby's diet on a one-at-a-time basis. After each vegetable is added, serve it for four or five days before introducing a new one. If any vegetable disagrees with the baby, it will show up in this period of time. A few symptoms of a food's disagreeing are skin rash, loose bowels, a sore diaper area, or frequent spitting up. If any of these symptoms occur, eliminate the new vegetable temporarily from his diet. Try it again in a month or two, when his digestive system is hardier, to see if there is any reaction.

Babies have very delicate, sensitive skin and can develop a skin rash around the mouth, and especially on the chin, when certain vegetables and fruits come in contact with that area. After you have finished feeding your baby, wash his face with warm water and apply a dab of baby lotion to prevent this type of irritation.

Don't be alarmed if your baby's bowel movements suddenly are not the customary color after he starts eating the new food. The undigested portion of certain vegetables will color his bowel movements —red for beets, yellow-orange for carrots and squash, and green for spinach and peas. Don't become frantic and imagine that he has a rare and exotic disease. Take a moment and think back to what he had to eat yesterday. That will usually be your answer.

Vegetables such as white potatoes, sweet potatoes or yams, peas, and lima beans are sometimes avoided by mothers who misguidedly think they are too starchy and high in calories. Remember that starches and calories are very important for a balanced diet. Don't carry over your own nutritional fads to the baby's diet. If you are trying to lose a couple of pounds, it is all right for you to eliminate starchy vegetables from your diet, but your baby needs them to provide vegetable protein, vitamins, and fuel for energy. A lunch that consists of only fruits and green vegetables would be marvelously high in vitamins but would be nutritionally lopsided; it would lack vegetable protein as well as the calories necessary for energy.

Cauliflower, cabbage, and broccoli have a tendency to produce gas within an immature digestive system. Wait until the baby is at least nine months to a year old before introducing these vegetables.

Baby's little system cannot handle corn kernels either. Don't even consider corn on the cob (or any whole-kernel corn for that matter) until he is two years old. He'll have plenty of time to picnic later.

Babies have a preference for carrots and squash because of their natural sweetness, but onions, Brussels sprouts, and turnips have such strong flavors that they are more acceptable to an older child. I have included them in the junior foods section.

These suggestions raise the age-old question: Are the taste buds of an infant developed enough to distinguish sweet from sour, bitter from salty? For me, the answer has been in the responsiveness of my own children to various tastes. We know that an infant is born with taste buds throughout his mouth—and therefore may be more discriminating than we may suppose. By the time we are adults, the taste buds have been reduced to small, concentrated areas on the tongue: sweetness and saltiness are tasted on the tip, sourness on the sides, and bitterness toward the back. We also know that all of the senses develop at different rates after birth, depending on function and needs. Vision and hearing develop somewhat later than touch, smell and taste. The point to remember is that all of the senses are functional to some degree at birth. So why not help expand the baby's sense of taste with wholesome, natural foods rather than processed ones whose manufacturers have been known to compensate for the lack of taste by adding monosodium glutamate, excessive salt, and other additives?

When you start to prepare vegetables for the baby, buy the freshest ones you can find and scrub them well, even though they are to be peeled. Cook them in a pan with a tight-fitting lid and in a small amount of water to shorten the cooking time. There may be a slight loss of color when this method is used, but the food value saved more than compensates for it. Many of the vitamins and minerals will dissolve in the water during cooking, so the cooking water should be saved and used as a thinner when you purée the vegetable. *Please, don't overcook your vegetables.* Overcooking lessens the nutritional value of food and destroys a great deal of its flavor.

At first, your baby should have one green or yellow vegetable a day. Vegetables are usually given at the 2 p.m. feeding, or close to the middle of the day. Start with a tablespoon or two, and gradually increase the portion to a quarter of a cup. Since meat is usually introduced into the diet at the same time as vegetables, your baby is now having a "lunch" of meat plus a vegetable.

As his appetite increases in the coming weeks, serve another vegetable, two or three times a week, in the evening along with his cereal and fruit.

Carrots

1 medium carrot
½ cup water
Pinch of salt

Scrub the carrot and cut off both ends. Scrape or peel it and cut into thin rounds.

Place in a small saucepan, add water and salt, and bring to a boil. Reduce the heat, cover, and simmer for 15 minutes. Drain the carrots, but do not discard the cooking liquid.

Purée the carrots, with 2 tablespoons of reserved liquid, in the blender or food mill. Yields about ¼ cup.

Carrots and Celery

This combination of vegetables is particularly smooth and fluffy. The celery adds cellulose, or roughage, to the baby's diet and stimulates bowel movements.

2 small, tender carrots
2 large ribs celery
¾ cup Chicken Broth (page 92) or Beef
    Bouillon (page 103)

Wash the carrots and celery. Peel or scrape carrots and remove celery strings with your vegetable peeler. Slice the carrots into thin rounds. Cut the celery into ½-inch pieces. Put the broth, carrots, and celery into a small saucepan. Cover and bring to a boil. Lower heat and simmer for 15 to 20 minutes, or until the vegetables are soft.

Lift the carrots and celery out of the broth with a slotted spoon and purée them in the blender or food mill. The celery contains enough natural liquid, so that no additional broth for thinning is necessary. Yields about 1 cup.

Squash

Fresh squash is available all year. Acorn and butternut squash are two winter varieties that are sweet-tasting and easy to mash. Zucchini, straight or crooknecked yellow, and cymling, or patty pan, are summer varieties that are moister, less starchy, and blander than winter squash, and are also delicate in flavor. The winter squash is a much sweeter vegetable than the summer varieties. All make wonderful baby food.

Acorn Squash

When you buy winter squash, make sure that the shell is very firm and that the squash feels heavy. The shell of the acorn squash is especially hard. For years I used to rummage through my husband's toolbox for his hammer. Then I would take my heaviest butcher knife, and using the hammer to hit the knife as if it were a chisel, I would smash my way through the squash. This is a very "unkitcheny" and slightly suicidal technique—don't use it! Eventually I discovered that a serrated knife designed for cutting frozen foods was perfect. With a sawing motion of this knife it is very easy to cut through anything, including the hardest squash. Now my husband goes through my kitchen drawers to find the knife whenever he needs a saw.

1 acorn squash or other small winter
   squash
1/2 cup water
3 tablespoons milk
1 teaspoon brown *or* white sugar
1/2 teaspoon butter

Preheat oven to 375°. Line a baking pan with aluminum foil. Scrub the squash very well with a vegetable brush and cut it in half. Remove the seeds from the squash and place the halves, cut side down, in the baking pan. Pour water around the squash, and cover pan loosely with foil. Bake for 30 minutes.

Turn the squash halves cut side up, cover again loosely with the foil, and continue baking for 30 minutes more.

Remove from oven and allow to cool. Scoop the pulp from the shells into the blender, and add the milk, sugar and butter. Blend until smooth. You can purée the squash in a food mill, too, but it won't be as smooth. Yields about 1 cup.

Steamed Zucchini

Zucchini is a slender green squash resembling a cucumber. A thin-skinned squash, it won't need sawing. Any of the other summer varieties of squash may be substituted in the following two recipes.

1 small zucchini
½ cup water
½ teaspoon butter (optional)
Pinch of salt

Scrub the zucchini. Peel and cut lengthwise into quarters, and then into small chunks. Put into a small saucepan, add water, and bring to a boil. Reduce heat, cover, and cook gently for 8 minutes, or until tender. Drain zucchini well, then purée in a blender or food mill until smooth. Add butter, if you like. Yields about ½ cup.

Baked Zucchini

1 small zucchini (about 4 to 5 inches long)
⅓ cup milk
Butter (about ½ teaspoon)

Preheat oven to 350°. Scrub the zucchini. Peel and cut lengthwise into quarters, and then into small chunks.

Place zucchini in a small baking pan with the milk and the butter. Cover tightly with aluminum foil and bake for 30 minutes.

Remove from oven and allow to cool. Drain well, and purée in a food mill or blender. Yields about ½ cup.

Spinach

Fresh raw spinach can be bought loose at the greengrocer's, or in plastic bags at the supermarket.

¼ pound fresh spinach
Pinch of salt
Butter (about ½ teaspoon)

Break off the large stems of the spinach and discard. Wash the leaves thoroughly in cold water until all sand and dirt have been removed. Drain well. Place in a small saucepan with salt (the water retained on the leaves will supply enough liquid for cooking). Cover the pan and cook for 12 minutes over a low heat. Turn the spinach once or twice with a fork while it is cooking. This prevents the spinach from matting down. Drain the spinach and purée in your food mill or blender. Add butter. Yields ½ cup.

Creamed Spinach

Use the preceding recipe to make puréed spinach and combine it with this quick white sauce:

4 tablespoons milk
1 teaspoon butter
Small pinch of salt
2 teaspoons cornstarch
2 teaspoons water

Heat milk, butter, and salt in a small saucepan until tiny bubbles form around the edges. Remove from heat.

Stir cornstarch in a small bowl with the water, and stir until you have a smooth paste. Add paste to the warm milk very slowly, stirring all the time (if paste is added too quickly, you'll end up with a panful of lumps).

Return sauce to the stove and cook over medium heat, stirring constantly until thickened—about 2 minutes.

Add the white sauce to 2 tablespoons of puréed spinach and stir until blended. Yields 1/3 cup.

Creamed Spinach with Egg

When the baby is old enough to eat egg yolk—about four months—push a hard-cooked yolk through a small strainer and sprinkle it on top of the spinach.

Green Beans or Wax Beans

1 cup fresh green or wax beans
Small pinch of salt
Butter (about 1/2 teaspoon, optional)

Wash beans and snap off both ends. Break into small pieces and place in a saucepan with just enough water to cover. Add salt. Cover and bring to a boil. Reduce heat and boil gently for 25 minutes, or until tender.

Remove beans with a slotted spoon and drain, reserving 2 tablespoons of the cooking liquid. Purée beans with reserved cooking liquid in your blender or food mill. Add butter if you like. Yields 1/2 cup.

Green Peas

½ pound fresh peas in the pod
1 lettuce leaf (optional)
Pinch of sugar
Pinch of salt
⅓ cup water

Wash and shell the peas, then wash them again along with two of the pods. Rinse the lettuce leaf. Place the pea pods, lettuce, sugar, salt and water in a small saucepan. (The lettuce and pods will add a touch of sweetness to the peas.) Cover and bring to a boil. Reduce heat and cook for 15 minutes. Drain peas, but save the lettuce and cooking liquid; discard pods. Purée peas and lettuce with 3 tablespoons of the cooking liquid in your blender or food mill until smooth. Yields ½ cup.

Sweet Potato and Apple

A plain baked sweet potato is delicious, but unless you have the oven going for other things, it's an extravagance to bake one potato for the baby. A potato prepared from this recipe is just as delicious and can be cooked on top of the stove.

1 small sweet potato or yam
½ medium apple
2 tablespoons milk
½ teaspoon butter
2 teaspoons brown sugar

Scrub and peel the sweet potato and cut it into ½-inch slices. Place the slices in a small pan with just enough water to cover. Cover and simmer for 10 minutes.

Meanwhile, wash and peel the apple, being sure to remove all of the seeds. Slice apple into thin pieces. Add apple slices to the sweet potato and continue to cook until both are soft—about 10 minutes more. Drain off cooking liquid. Purée sweet potato and apple, with milk, butter, and brown sugar, in your blender or food mill until smooth. Depending on the size of the sweet potato you may need an extra tablespoon or two of milk to achieve a smooth consistency. Yields about 1 cup.

NOTE: For a different flavor, orange or other fruit juice may be substituted for the milk.

Whipped Potato

1 small baking potato
2 tablespoons milk
Pinch of salt (optional)
Butter (about 1/2 teaspoon)

Scrub and peel the potato. Cut into quarters and place in a small saucepan with enough water to cover. Bring to a boil and simmer, uncovered, for 20 minutes, or until potato can be easily pierced with a fork. Drain, reserving 2 tablespoons of cooking liquid. Purée the potato, 2 tablespoons of the cooking liquid, and milk, salt, and butter in your food mill or electric mixer (the blender is not very satisfactory for potatoes). Yields about 1/3 cup.

Potato and Carrot

1 small baking potato
1/2 small carrot
1/4 rib celery
1 sprig parsley
1 slice onion (for a little flavor)
2 tablespoons milk
Butter (about 1/2 teaspoon, optional)
Pinch of salt (optional)

Scrub potato, carrot, and celery. Wash the parsley. Peel the potato, carrot, and onion, and remove strings from the celery. Cut the potato and carrot into small pieces.

Place all ingredients, except the milk, butter and salt in a small saucepan with enough water to cover. Bring to a boil. Cover the pan, but leave the lid slightly to one side; reduce heat slightly and boil vegetables gently for 25 minutes, or until soft. Discard celery, parsley, and onion. Drain potato and carrot but save the cooking liquid.

Purée potato and carrot in your food mill or blender with 2 tablespoons of the cooking liquid and the milk. The butter and salt may be added, if you wish, for taste. Yields about 2/3 cup.

NOTE: If you have a choice between a food mill and a blender, use the food mill for this recipe—it retains the original texture of the potato and carrot better.

Vichyssoise

If you add 6 tablespoons of milk instead of 2 to this recipe, you can make the baby his first Vichyssoise.

Beets

Choose the smallest beets you can find. If beets are longer than 1½ inches in diameter, they will need a longer cooking time and will tend to have a coarser texture.

4 small fresh beets
Pinch of salt (optional)
5 tablespoons broth or orange juice

Scrub beets well. Cut off all but an inch or so of the tops. Do not peel.

Place in a small saucepan and half cover with water. Cover and bring to a boil. Reduce heat and boil gently for 35 minutes, or until beets are fork-tender. Allow to cool.

Drain and discard the cooking liquid. Slip skins off the beets and cut into small pieces. Purée in blender or food mill with the broth or orange juice. Add salt if you like. Yields about 1 cup.

meats and poultry

AT ABOUT THREE MONTHS

Meats and poultry are the first solid foods your baby gets that contain a substantial amount of protein, the body-building material needed for growth. All meats—beef, lamb, veal, liver, turkey, pork, and chicken—have high nutritional value. However, lamb and chicken are the easiest to digest, so it's a good idea to start with these. Broil, braise or stew the meat. Foods fried in butter, solid vegetable shortening, or oil are too difficult for the baby to digest.

Meat is usually introduced into the baby's diet at the same time as vegetables, about the age of three months. A baby, until he is a year old, needs one ounce of meat each day. Of course, when he is old enough to eat eggs, cheese, and fish, these foods can be substituted for meat. Lunchtime is the usual time for serving meat and a vegetable.

Start with two or three teaspoons of puréed meat, and increase the portion to a quarter of a cup.

Since you will be preparing the meats yourself, your child will not be consuming flavor additives or food preservatives, but even at home, some precautions must be taken. For example, all of the skin of chicken and turkey should be removed before cooking. Poultry farmers use chemical steroids in chicken feed to raise the largest birds in the shortest period of time. With the aid of these chemicals, they have been able to shorten the growing time of broiling chickens by one third. Research has shown that these steroids accumulate primarily in the skin of the birds. Though there is no definite proof at this time that steroids will harm your baby—and, in fact, there may never be —I see no reason for adding them to an infant's diet. Scientists are now questioning the cumulative effects of drugs, chemicals, and insecticides on man over a long period of time, and it seems sensible to try to avoid them. Home-cooked puréed meats give you the assurance that your baby is eating wholesome meat, and they are so delicious I can't imagine anyone feeding their baby anything else.

In order to achieve the smoothest texture for puréed meats, it is necessary to use a blender—a food mill will just *not* do. When you start blending small quantities of meat, you may find that the food swirls to the sides of the blender container and will not fall back to the blades. I suggest you refer to page 53 to see how to avoid this.

Store the puréed meats in small containers with tight-fitting lids in the coldest part of your refrigerator. Use the meats within two days after you have cooked them. Puréed meats freeze very well, so if you have prepared more than can be eaten in two days, freeze the rest in individual portions. Frozen meats prepared for the baby must be used within two months.

Chicken is lower in fat and calories than other meats, but it has the same amount of protein and is far less expensive than beef, lamb, or veal. A chicken that is labeled broiler or fryer is the youngest and most tender poultry you can buy, so you should use it for the baby. However, if you are preparing a roasting chicken, capon, or Thanksgiving turkey for the family dinner, you can purée a few slices of white and dark meat with some fat-free natural gravy and vegetable cooking liquid to make a delicious dinner for your baby. I have found that a mixture of white and dark meat creates the best consistency of baby food—the white meat is smooth in texture, the dark meat is moist. The combination is just right.

Fried chicken is too hard to digest, and broiled chicken tends to be dry, so I do not recommend them for making baby food.

To store fresh chicken, remove the tight plastic film wrapping, rewrap the chicken loosely in aluminum foil, fresh plastic wrap, or heavy waxed paper, and place it in the coldest spot in your refrigerator. You can store raw chicken on the refrigerator shelf for a day or two. Cooked chicken must be covered for storage. It can be stored in the refrigerator for one or two days. Raw chicken can be prepared for the freezer and stored for as long as six months if the freezer temperature is zero or below. Cooked or puréed chicken must be used within two months. To thaw frozen raw chicken, keep it, wrapped, in the refrigerator (not at room temperature) for twenty-four hours, or until it has thawed. Do not refreeze thawed raw chicken. (Of course, you can refreeze it after it has been cooked.)

All of the following chicken recipes freeze well. Take advantage of this by doubling or tripling the recipes. Use one serving the day it is prepared and freeze the rest in small containers for individual servings. Be sure to label and date each container.

Any broth that is not used in puréeing the chicken should be frozen in an ice-cube tray and stored as frozen "bouillon cubes," as described in the chicken-broth recipes. Use the cubes with vegetables and pastina. They will add a wonderful flavor, and also add the nourishment that has dissolved from the chicken into the broth. And on days when your baby has an upset tummy, what could be nicer than a little chicken soup?

Chicken Broth

Half of a broiler or fryer chicken
1/4 teaspoon salt
1 small carrot
1 small piece (1 inch) parsnip
1 rib celery
1/4 small onion
2 sprigs parsley

Remove skin from chicken and rinse meat under cold running water. Place chicken in a medium-sized saucepan, cover with water, and add salt. Bring to a boil and skim off any foam. Meanwhile, wash and scrape the carrot and parsnip. Wash celery and remove strings with your vegetable peeler. Peel and wash the onion. Cut into quarters. Wash the parsley. Cut vegetables into 1/2-inch pieces and add to the chicken. Cover saucepan, but leave lid slightly ajar to allow the steam to escape. Simmer gently for 45 minutes or until the chicken is very tender.

Strain the broth. Pour it into a clean ice-cube tray and freeze. When solid, gently release the handle of the tray and you will have individual frozen bouillon cubes. An average ice tray will make cubes that are equivalent to about 1 1/2 tablespoons of liquid broth. Wrap cubes individually in plastic wrap or aluminum foil and store them all together in a tightly closed plastic bag in your freezer. *Do not* leave them exposed in an open ice-cube tray.

If you discard the bones, onion, and parsnip, you can use the chicken meat and the other vegetables for the baby's dinner or in the recipes listed below. I often use the chicken to make salad or creamed chicken for my own lunch.

Chicken in the Pot

This recipe is the basic one for preparing Puréed Chicken, Vegetables with Chicken Broth, Chicken with Vegetables, and Chicken Fricassee. Add a tomato to the chicken when you add the other vegetables, and you'll have your baby's first Chicken Cacciatore.

If you have any broth left over from any of these recipes, freeze it as described in the Chicken Broth recipe.

½ chicken breast
1 chicken thigh
1 small carrot
1 small piece (1 inch) parsnip (optional)
1 rib celery
1 sprig parsley
1 slice onion
1⅓ cups water
¼ teaspoon salt

Remove and discard the chicken skin and rinse the meat under cold running water. Wash the vegetables. Scrape the carrot and parsnip, and cut them into small pieces. Remove celery strings with your vegetable peeler and cut into small pieces also. Rinse the parsley and peel the onion slice. Place chicken in a medium-sized saucepan with the water and salt. Bring to a boil and skim off any foam. Cover partially and simmer for 30 minutes. Add vegetables and cook for 30 minutes more. Lift chicken and vegetables from the broth with a slotted spoon. Discard the onion. Save the broth and set aside the other vegetables.

Puréed Chicken

Remove chicken meat from the bones and cut into small pieces. Purée with 6 tablespoons of broth in your blender until you have a smooth paste (you may have to stop the blender and scrape down the sides of the container 3 or 4 times). Depending on the size of the chicken, you may need additional broth for making the purée. Yields about 1¼ cups.

Vegetables with Chicken Broth

Purée the carrot, celery, parsnip, and parsley in the blender. You probably won't need additional broth to make a delicious vegetable to accompany the chicken. Yields about ½ cup.

You may also purée the chicken and vegetables together, with 4 tablespoons of broth. Yields about 1½ cups.

Chicken Fricassee

Ingredients for Chicken in the Pot (see preceding recipe)
1 small potato
6 tablespoons milk

Prepare ingredients for Chicken in the Pot and begin the cooking.

Meanwhile, scrub and peel the potato and dice into small pieces. After the chicken has cooked for 30 minutes, add the potato along with the other vegetables. Cook 30 minutes more. Discard the celery, parsley, and parsnip, but save the broth to freeze. Purée the chicken, carrot, and potato in the blender with the milk until smooth and creamy. You may need an additional tablespoon or two of milk, depending on the size of the potato. Yields 1 ¾ cups.

Roast Chicken or Turkey, Family Style

Follow this recipe for the baby's meal if you are roasting chicken or turkey for the family dinner. Instead of puréeing the meat with broth, you can use the fat-free natural gravy of the chicken or turkey. The best way to skim off all the fat from the natural gravy is to pour it into a bowl and refrigerate. The fat will rise to the top and harden and can be lifted off easily with a spoon. You can also remove the fat at room temperature with a baster. Serve blander vegetables with the regular family dinner that can be puréed and shared with the baby—such as peas, green beans, or carrots, instead of Brussels sprouts, broccoli, or cauliflower.

½ cup cooked white meat, cubed
½ cup cooked dark meat, cubed
4 tablespoons natural gravy, fat-free
6 tablespoons cooking liquid from any bland vegetable

Purée diced chicken or turkey in your blender with the gravy and vegetable cooking liquid. Blend until very smooth. Yields about 1 cup.

A lamb is a sheep under one year of age. Meat from sheep older than one year is referred to as mutton. Though lamb is available twelve months a year, young lamb is most plentiful between January and March, when the prices are usually lowest. The color of lamb darkens with the age of the animal. A very young, milk-fed lamb will have light, pinkish meat, but the lamb that is most readily available in supermarkets is usually pinkish-red, indicating that the animal is between six months and one year old.

The fat of lamb is smooth, white, and rather brittle, and is covered with a thin, transparent, parchment-like tissue called fell. You should remove as much of the fat as possible before preparing lamb for your baby.

If you are planning a roast leg of lamb for Sunday dinner, or if you are broiling chops or making a lamb stew for the rest of the family, count the baby in, too. He can have all of these dishes in puréed form. When buying lamb don't overlook shoulder chops— you get much more meat for a lot less money, and this less expensive cut is every bit as nutritious and tasty as the costlier rib or loin chops.

When you prepare lamb dishes for the baby only, you should use stewing lamb because it purées best. The two choice cuts for stewing are lamb shanks and lamb shoulder.

Puréed lamb, with or without vegetables, freezes well, so double the following recipes from time to time and you will have a great selection of frozen meats and vegetables at your fingertips, ready to serve when needed.

To store fresh lamb, remove the tight plastic wrapping and re-cover it *loosely* with aluminum foil, heavy waxed paper, or fresh plastic wrap. Place it in the coldest section of your refrigerator. Raw chops can be stored in the refrigerator for two or three days, raw stew meat for two days, and roasts for four or five days. Raw lamb can be kept frozen for six to seven months at 0°. To thaw frozen raw lamb, keep it in the refrigerator, wrapped (not at room temperature) for twelve to twenty-four hours, depending on the amount, or until it has thawed. Do not refreeze thawed raw lamb. (Of course, you can refreeze it after it has been cooked.) Cooked, puréed lamb can be stored frozen for only two to three months. Once thawed, it should never be refrozen.

Rib or Shoulder Lamb Chop

1 small rib or shoulder lamb chop
¼ teaspoon salt
½ cup water

Trim fat from the chop and wipe with a damp paper towel. Sear the chop in a hot, dry skillet; *do not* add oil or butter. Brown quickly on both sides— this should take a half-minute for each side. Add 3 tablespoons of the water to the skillet, lower heat, and cover tightly. Cook for 5 minutes, turn the chop, and cook for 5 minutes more.

Remove the chop from the pan and cut into small pieces. Add remaining 4 tablespoons of water to juices that remain in the frying pan and set over a medium-to-high heat until well blended. Purée the lamb in your blender with 3 tablespoons of the pan juice until smooth. A rib chop yields about ¼ cup, and a shoulder lamb chop about ⅓ cup.

Lamb Chop with Potato

1 small rib, loin, or shoulder lamb chop
½ cup water
¼ teaspoon salt
1 small potato

Following the preceding recipe, cook the chop and prepare pan juices.

Meanwhile, scrub and peel the potato. Cut into small pieces and place in a saucepan with salt and enough water to cover. Bring to a boil and simmer, uncovered, for 20 minutes or until done. Drain potato and purée with the cut-up chop and 3 tablespoons of pan juices. Add another tablespoon of lamb juice, if necessary, to achieve a smooth consistency. Yields about ¾ cup.

For a tasty change, substitute a sweet potato for the white potato.

Puréed Lamb

If you use lamb shank, ask your butcher to saw the shank into three or four pieces. Shoulder of lamb should be cubed.

1 pound lamb shank with bone, in 3 or 4 pieces *or* ½ pound boned lamb shoulder, in 1-inch cubes
2 cups water
2 small potatoes
1 small carrot
1 rib celery
1 small tomato
1 sprig parsley
1 slice onion
¼ teaspoon salt

Trim all fat from the meat, rinse, and wipe with a damp paper towel. Sear the lamb pieces in a hot, dry, heavy saucepan; *do not* add oil or butter to the pan. Turn the meat to brown all sides quickly so that it doesn't stick to the pan. Add water and salt and cover tightly. Cook slowly for 1 hour.

While the meat is cooking, prepare the vegetables. Wash all the vegetables thoroughly. Peel the potatoes and carrot. Remove celery strings with your vegetable peeler. Peel onion. Wash parsley. Dice the vegetables into small pieces.

After the meat has cooked for an hour, add the vegetables and parsley and continue cooking for 30 minutes more. Salt lightly.

Remove the meat from the pan (save the broth and vegetables) and trim off the gristle. Cut the meat into small pieces and purée in your blender with ¾ cup broth. Yields about 1½ cups.

Vegetables with Lamb Broth

Puree the potatoes, carrot, celery, tomato, and parsley (discard onion) in the blender or food mill to make a delicious vegetable dish to accompany the lamb. Yields about ½ cup.

Baby's Lamb Stew

For a delicious introduction to lamb stew, discard onion and purée the lamb, potatoes, carrot, celery, tomato, and parsley in the blender with ½ cup of broth until you have a smooth consistency. Yields about 2 cups.

VEAL

The best veal is from very young calves, those between four to fourteen weeks old. It is most abundant in winter and spring.

The color of veal varies with the age of the animal. Very young milk-fed veal is grayish-pink in color and has very little or no fat marbling. The meat becomes redder and there is more fat as the animal ages.

If you are planning a veal roast or a veal stew with vegetables, your baby can share in the meal, enjoying his puréed version. The best cuts of veal for any veal stew are shanks and boneless shoulder. Chops and cutlets are also fine unless they are breaded and fried, in which case they are not suitable for baby food.

To store raw veal, remove the tight plastic wrap from the packaged meat and cover the meat loosely with aluminum foil, heavy waxed paper, or plastic wrap. Place in the coldest section of the refrigerator. Fresh chops, roasts, stew cuts, and cutlets can be stored in the refrigerator for two to three days, frozen veal for six to seven months in a freezer. When you are thawing raw veal, leave the wrapping on and place it in the refrigerator for twelve to twenty-four hours, depending on the size. Never refreeze the veal once it has been defrosted. Of course, once the veal has been cooked it can be frozen. All of the following cooked veal dishes can be frozen and stored for two to three months. Remember to label and date the containers before freezing.

Puréed Veal

¼ pound veal shoulder
1 small carrot
1 rib celery
1 small tomato
2 sprigs parsley
¼ small onion
1 cup water
¼ teaspoon salt

Trim gristle and fat from meat, then wipe with a damp paper towel. Wash vegetables and parsley. Scrape carrot. Remove celery strings with a vegetable peeler. Peel onion. Dice the vegetables. Place the veal, water, and salt in a saucepan and bring to a boil. Skim off any foam. Add onion, cover, and simmer for 45 minutes. Add the other vegetables and cook 30 minutes more.

Lift meat and vegetables from the broth with a slotted spoon. Save the broth and vegetables. Cut veal into small pieces. Purée diced veal in your blender with ¾ cup broth. Yields about 1 cup.

Vegetables with Veal Broth

Discard onion. Purée remaining vegetables together in your blender or food mill for a delicious taste medley. Yields 1/3 cup.

Veal with Vegetables

Discard onion. Purée diced veal and vegetables with 1/2 cup broth. Blend until smooth. Yields 1 1/2 cups.

Veal with Rice and Vegetables

1 small veal shin (about 1/2 pound)
1 small carrot
1/4 small onion
1/2 rib celery
2 sprigs parsley
1 small tomato
1 1/2 cups water
1/4 teaspoon salt
2 tablespoons precooked instant rice

Trim gristle and fat from meat, and wipe it with a damp paper towel. Wash vegetables. Peel carrot and onion. Scrape strings from celery. Cut carrot into pieces. Place the veal, water, and salt into a saucepan and bring to a boil. Skim off any foam. Add the onion, cover, and simmer for 45 minutes. Then add remaining vegetables and cook for 15 minutes more. Add rice, straight from the box, and cook for an additional 20 minutes.

Lift the veal from the broth with a slotted spoon. Cut meat away from the bone and dice it into small pieces. Strain and save the broth. Discard the onion. Purée the veal, vegetables, and rice in your blender with enough broth to make a smooth consistency. Yields about 1 cup.

❖◈❖

BEEF

❖◈❖

The beef available from your supermarket or butcher is graded and stamped according to the conformation (or build) of the animal, the quality of the meat and the proportion of meat to fat. Beef of good quality has extensive marbling (fat mixed in with the meat), and firm fine-textured meat of light-red to deep-red color. The retail grades of beef, in descending order of quality, are prime, choice, good, and standard. Following these are lower grades of meat used in sausage and other processed meats. Prime beef is usually available only to restaurants and fancy butcher shops. Choice and good grades of beef are sold by supermarket chains and butcher shops. These are excellent cuts, well marbled and tender.

Use dry heat (broiling and roasting) for more tender cuts of beef, such as steaks and rib roasts, and use moist heat (stewing and pot roasting) for less tender cuts, such as chuck and round.

If you are planning roast beef or broiled steak for your family's dinner, you can purée either one for the baby's meal by blending his share with some of the pan juices from which you have removed all fat. This also applies if you're planning a hearty beef stew unless it has been made with wine or is heavily spiced. Simply spoon out several pieces of beef to about 6 ounces and purée them with a small amount of fat-free broth. This should yield about 1½ cups of puréed beef. Your baby will be enjoying the same deli-

cious flavor and nourishment from a carefully prepared stew as the rest of the family, with no extra fuss for you.

Whenever you are preparing beef dishes just for the baby, you should use cuts of stewing beef. Although these are among the most inexpensive cuts, they are as high in protein as filet mignon. Boned beef shoulder, beef shank and beef shin are good for stewing, but the most popular cut for stew is chuck. It is usually found in the meat case already cut into cubes and simply labeled "stewing beef." The best cut of chuck to buy whole is boneless middle chuck, sometimes referred to as chuck filet. Ask for chuck filet with an air of authority and casually tell the butcher not to include any neck or blade. The butcher will be awed, and you'll have a nice piece of beef.

To store fresh beef, remove the tight plastic wrap and rewrap it loosely with aluminum foil, heavy waxed paper, or plastic wrap. Place the meat in the coldest section of your refrigerator. You should use raw ground beef the same day you buy it. You can store raw stewing beef for one to two days, raw steaks for two to three days and raw roasts for three to four days. To freeze beef, wrap it tightly in aluminum foil or freezer paper and seal it air-tight. In a freezer, raw beef can be kept frozen for six to eight months, cooked puréed beef for two to three months. Never refreeze thawed *cooked* beef.

Thaw frozen beef in the refrigerator (not at room temperature), wrapped. This will take twelve to twenty-four hours depending on the amount of meat. Never refreeze raw beef after it has defrosted. Of course, once it has been cooked it can be frozen.

The following beef recipes freeze well, so use one serving and freeze the rest in individual serving containers.

Puréed Beef

½ pound beef chuck, cut into 1-inch cubes
1 soupbone (beef-shin bone), split
1½ cups water
¼ cup salt
1 small carrot
1 rib celery
½ small onion
2 sprigs parsley
3 to 5 green beans
1 small tomato

Trim off fat and wipe meat and soupbone with a damp paper towel. Wash vegetables. Scrape carrot; remove strings from celery; peel onion. Remove the ends of the string beans and slice them. Quarter the tomato and cut up the carrot. Heat a heavy saucepan (*do not* add oil or butter) and brown meat and soupbone, turning frequently. Add water and salt and bring to a boil. Skim off any foam. Add the onion, cover and simmer for 1 hour. Add the remaining vegetables and cook for 20 minutes more.

Strain the broth and save it and the vegetables. Purée the vegetables in your blender as a side dish with the puréed beef.

Cut meat into small pieces and purée in your blender with 1 cup of the broth until it has a smooth consistency. Yields about 1½ cups.

Beef and Barley Soup

There is something about the name "beef and barley soup" that sounds like something brimming over with good flavor, nutrition, and old-fashioned stick-to-the-ribs ingredients. Here is the way to make this hearty concoction for the littlest member of the family.

Ingredients for Puréed Beef (see above) with water increased to 2 cups.
1 tablespoon fine barley
1 cup water

Use fine barley for the baby. There are two kinds available. One type has to be soaked in water for 12 hours before it is used. The other type can be added directly to the stew or soup without soaking. If you can find the ready-to-cook kind, use it. It saves you the whole process of thinking about what you are going to do tomorrow, when you'll be happy enough just to get through today.

If you can't find the ready-to-cook variety, soak barley in the cup of water overnight. Boil barley in the same water for 15 minutes. Drain barley and discard the water. Meanwhile, prepare the Puréed Beef, using the increased amount of water.

Add the barley to the meat and onions. Cover and simmer for 1 hour. Add the vegetables and cook 20 minutes more. Strain the broth and save for later use. Cut meat into small pieces, and purée in the blender with vegetables (discard onion), barley and ⅔ cup of broth until smooth. Add a little more broth if necessary. Yields about 2¼ cups.

Meatball Soup

When this recipe is made in family-size quantities, it is one of our favorites. For grownups, I cook it in a big soup pot with half a green pepper and ½ teaspoon of freshly ground black pepper. And, of course, I don't purée it. If you would like to make it for your own dinner sometime, double or triple the ingredients depending on the size of your family. The following recipe is just for the baby.

¼ pound ground round or ground lean chuck
1½ tablespoons precooked instant rice
3 tablespoons water
½ teaspoon salt
½ small carrot
½ rib celery
1 slice onion
1 small, fresh tomato
1 small potato

Scrub and scrape the carrot and celery, removing the celery strings. Peel and wash the slice of onion. Rinse the tomato and remove stem. Scrub and peel the potato. Dice the carrot, celery, and potato. Cut tomato in half.

Place ground meat in a bowl. Add rice, straight from the box, together with water and salt. Mix thoroughly, and gently form into 7 or 8 small meatballs. Bring 1¾ cups water to a boil in a saucepan. Drop in meatballs and bring to a boil again. Skim off any foam. Boil gently, uncovered, for 25 minutes, then add vegetables and simmer 20 minutes longer.

Lift meat and vegetables out of the broth with a slotted spoon and purée in your blender or food mill. Yields about 1 cup.

Broth

Strain the broth and refrigerate it if you're planning to use it within the next day or two; for longer storage, pour it in a small container and freeze it.

Roast Beef

Follow this recipe if you are having roast beef for the family dinner. Use some natural beef gravy, free of fat, and vegetable cooking liquid in making the purée. Serve the family a bland vegetable that can be puréed and shared with the baby.

1 cup cubed roast beef, all fat removed
4 tablespoons natural gravy, free of fat
6 tablespoons vegetable cooking liquid

Dice roast beef into small pieces and purée in your blender with beef gravy and vegetable cooking liquid. Yields 1 cup.

Beef Bouillon

Soupbones give beef bouillon rich color and flavor. Ask the butcher to split some shin bones, preferably with some meat on them, to make beef stock.

1 pound beef chuck
3 pounds soupbones
1 large carrot
1 rib celery
3 sprigs parsley
1 small tomato
$\frac{1}{2}$ small onion
2 quarts water
$\frac{1}{4}$ teaspoon salt
$\frac{1}{2}$ small bay leaf

Preheat oven to 350°. Wipe meat and bones with a damp paper towel. Wash vegetables. Scrape carrot and celery, removing strings from celery. Quarter the tomato and peel the onion. Brown the bones in the oven in a small soup pot for about an hour, turning the bones after the first 30 minutes. Re-move pot from oven and place on top of stove.

Add the chuck, water, and salt and bring to a boil, skimming off any foam. Add vegetables and bay leaf. Cover the pot, but leave the lid slightly to one side to allow steam to escape. Simmer gently for 2½ hours.

Strain broth through cheesecloth or a fine sieve. Save the meat, discard bones and vegetables. Cool broth, un-covered. Skim off any fat, then pour broth into an ice-cube tray and freeze. When solid, gently release the handle of the tray and you will have frozen beef-bouillon cubes, each equivalent to approximately 1½ tablespoons of liq-uid broth if your tray is of average size. Wrap cubes individually in plastic wrap or aluminum foil and store them in a closed plastic bag in your freezer. *Do not* leave them exposed in an open ice-cube tray.

Boiled Beef

Cut up the beef and purée it with any bland vegetable cooking liquid (or a little of the beef broth if you like). Or slice it cold, for tasty sandwiches for your own lunch.

❖◇

PORK

❖◇

Pork is a rich and rather fatty meat, an excellent source of vitamins, and is a pleasant change of taste. If you get lean pork, from a young animal, it will be pale pink—almost white—with white fat. The most popular methods of cooking pork are to roast the larger joints and to grill or fry the chops. If you are going to have roast pork for dinner, purée an ounce or so, with the natural gravy, with fat removed, for the baby. Or prepare a small chop, trimmed of the fat, and cooked, un-breaded, in a hot, dry pan. Since pork is rich, a side dish of something cool and sharp—applesauce or puréed apri-cots—would be nice to complete the menu.

If not thoroughly cooked, fresh pork may sometimes be responsible for a serious disease called trichinosis. How-ever, the trichinae perish at quite a low temperature—around 135 degrees—and if pork is cooked thoroughly they are destroyed.

To store fresh pork, remove the tight plastic wrapping and re-cover it loosely with aluminum foil, heavy waxed paper, or plastic wrap. Place it in the coldest section of your refrigerator. Raw pork can be stored in the refrigerator for two to three days and it can be kept frozen for five to six months at 0°. Cooked pork can be frozen for two to three months. To thaw raw pork, allow it to defrost in the refrigerator, wrapped, for twelve to twenty-four hours, depending on the quantity of meat. Never refreeze pork once it has thawed.

Pork Chops

1 small rib or loin pork chop
¼ teaspoon salt
¾ cup water

Trim fat from chop and wipe with a damp paper towel. Sear the chop in a hot dry skillet—do not add oil or butter. Brown quickly on both sides over a medium heat—this should take about half a minute for each side. Add ½ cup of the water to the skillet, lower heat and cover tightly. Cook for twenty minutes, turn the chop and add extra water to the broth if necessary. Cook 20 minutes more.

Remove the chop from the pan and cut the meat into small pieces. Add remaining ¼ cup water to the juices remaining in the pan and heat over a medium flame until well blended. Purée the pork in your blender with 4 tablespoons of the pan juice until smooth. Yields about ⅓ cup.

Braised Pork with Sweet Potato

½ pound pork shoulder, cut into 1-inch cubes
1 small sweet potato
¼ teaspoon salt
2 cups water

Trim off all the fat, then wipe the meat with a damp paper towel. Scrub and peel the sweet potato; cut into four pieces. Brown the pork on all sides in a hot, dry heavy saucepan—do not add oil or butter. Add the water and salt and bring to a boil. Cover tightly and simmer for 1 hour, adding more water if necessary. Add the sweet potato and cook 15 minutes more. Lift the meat and potato out of the broth. Cut the meat into small pieces and purée in the blender with the sweet potato and 1 cup of the broth. Yields about 1¾ cups.

LIVER

Liver is one of the most nutritious foods you can give your baby. It is an excellent source of protein, iron, vitamin A, riboflavin, and niacin, and it even contains a trace of vitamin C. But with all this, liver is being scrutinized by scientists—as are many of the foods we eat today—for possible harmfulness.

The liver's function as part of an animal's filtering system makes it a storehouse for impurities from the digestive system that are on their way to the blood. This is why the liver of animals—like the heart, kidneys and other vital organs—may contain traces of pesticides and other chemicals, along with the beneficial and necessary substances.

Both man and animal life are constantly exposed to environmental pollutants in the form of radioactive elements, fumes, smoke, detergents, pesticides, and a vast variety of industrial wastes. We come in contact with them every day in the air we breathe, the water we drink and the food we eat. The core of the pollution controversy is based on what is called cumulative effect, which means that a good many years will be needed to determine the effects of these factors. What is the cumulative effect on man of eating beef, calf, or pig liver over a long period of time? We just don't know.

There are scientists who feel that you should never eat another piece of liver again, and there are scientists who feel that the amounts of harmful elements contained in liver are small and insignificant. In feeding my own family, I have decided that because liver is a valuable source of iron and protein, until there is conclusive proof that there is danger in consuming it, the nutritional value outweighs any harm that could result from eating liver. You, of course, may come to a different conclusion, and may decide not to feed liver to your baby.

To store fresh liver, remove the tight plastic wrap and rewrap it loosely with aluminum foil, heavy waxed paper, or plastic wrap. Place it in the coldest section of your refrigerator. You can store raw liver in your refrigerator for one to two days, cooked liver for two to three days. To freeze liver, wrap tightly in aluminum foil or freezer paper and seal so that it is air-tight. Uncooked liver can be stored safely in the freezer for six months. The baby's puréed cooked liver can remain frozen for two months. To thaw frozen liver, place in the refrigerator, wrapped, until defrosted—about six to seven hours. Never refreeze thawed raw liver. Of course, once it has been cooked it can be frozen. Do not refreeze thawed *cooked* liver.

Liver Pâté

The very first time I cooked liver for my younger baby, I was tempted to slip it underneath the sweet potatoes so that she wouldn't see what she was eating. I guess I just assumed that all babies instinctively disliked liver. However, I tasted it myself and it was so good, almost like a smooth pâté, that I decided to serve it undisguised. I gave her a tiny taste, and she loved it. Moral of this story: please don't hide the liver! Your baby will probably like it, and the time to develop his taste for new foods is now.

½ pound calf's liver
¾ cup chicken or beef broth

Wipe liver with a damp paper towel. Place liver and broth in a small saucepan and bring to a boil. Reduce heat and simmer for 7 minutes. Remove liver (reserve broth) and strip off any tough membranes. Cut liver into small pieces and purée in your blender with 4 tablespoons of broth. The liver will be very smooth and fluffy in texture. Yields about 1 cup.

NOTE: Puréed liver becomes solid once it has been refrigerated. To reheat for serving, you will need to stir in about one tablespoon of broth or water with the meat.

Juices

AT ABOUT FOUR MONTHS

When your baby is about three and a half to four months old, it is usually the time to add juices to his diet. (The baby's doctor will tell you when to start.) Juice can be fresh, frozen, or canned specially for babies. I've always squeezed my own citrus-fruit juices, because the natural vitamin C is destroyed during the canning process (this is why canned juices are fortified with synthetic vitamin C).

Five months is a good age to introduce juice in a cup to your baby. This will be a new and enjoyable experience for both you and your baby. There are plastic cups called dribble cups, which have a spout and a lid to prevent most of the liquid from spilling.

Of course, your baby will still be drinking his milk from a bottle, but using the cup for juice is the first step in weaning. Your baby will use his sucking reflex to drink from the cup and some juice will dribble down his chin, so don't forget his bib. Wash his face with warm water when he is finished to avoid any possibility of a skin irritation.

For a change of taste from orange juice, try canned pineapple-grapefruit juice, and apple juice. The pineapple-grapefruit drink is fortified with vitamin C, but since apple juice is very low in this important vitamin, don't substitute it for orange juice. Both of these juices are sweet and babies really enjoy them.

Orange Juice

Babies usually have a liking for orange juice and have few digestive problems with it, but once in a while a baby will develop a rash, usually in the diaper area, from the citric acid. If this happens, try again in a month or two.

1 orange
Cooled boiled water

Wash orange and cut in half. Squeeze juice and strain it through a fine sieve.

Start with the juice of half an orange diluted with 2 tablespoons of cooled boiled water. Over the next month, gradually decrease the proportion of water and increase the juice until he is drinking 2 or 3 ounces of plain orange juice.

Strain the juice during the first few months through a fine sieve so that the pulp doesn't clog the nipple or the small openings of the dribble cup. When your baby is old enough to use an ordinary glass, it won't be necessary to strain the juice.

A child under three years of age needs a minimum of 40 milligrams of vitamin C a day. Of course, many juices contain vitamin C, but the amounts vary so much that I am including a chart to show you the quantities in each one. Above all, don't warm your baby's juice, because heat destroys vitamin C.

Vitamin C per Each 3 Ounces of Juice

Orange juice	Fresh	50 mg
	Canned (vitamin C added)	40 mg
	Frozen (standard dilution)	45 mg
Grapefruit	Fresh	38 mg
	Canned (vitamin C added)	30 mg
	Frozen (standard dilution)	33 mg
Lemonade	Fresh	21 mg
	Frozen (standard dilution)	7 mg
Apple juice	Canned	1 mg
Grape juice	Bottled	a trace
	Frozen (standard dilution)	4 mg
	Fortified grapejuice drink	16 mg
Tomato juice	Canned	16 mg
	Vegetable cocktail	16 mg
Pineapple grapefruit	Canned	20 mg

Grapefruit Juice

1 grapefruit
Cooled boiled water
1 teaspoon sugar *or* honey

Wash grapefruit and cut it in half. Squeeze one half and strain juice through a fine sieve. Add 1 teaspoon of sugar or honey for sweetening. (Wrap remaining half in plastic wrap and refrigerate it for later use.)

NOTE: Start with the juice of half a grapefruit diluted with 4 tablespoons of cooled boiled water. Over the next month, gradually decrease the proportion of water and increase the amount of juice until the baby is drinking 2 or 3 ounces of plain grapefruit juice. Strain the juice through a fine sieve during the first few months so that the pulp doesn't clog the nipple or the openings of the drinking cup.

Lemonade

Even a four-month-old will enjoy a cool drink of lemonade.

1 lemon
½ cup cooled boiled water
1 tablespoon sugar

Wash lemon, cut it in half, and squeeze and strain the juice. Add water and sugar; stir. Serve in baby's dribble cup.

Eggs

At about the age of four months many babies start eating eggs. Your doctor may suggest that you use only the yolk, but it is becoming more and more common to start the baby right off with the whole egg. If your baby has adjusted well to new foods, the whole-egg approach seems very sensible, and much easier on the cook.

Eggs can be served for breakfast, lunch, or dinner. They are easy to cook in a variety of ways, and they are a great source of protein and fat. Before breaking a raw egg, it's always a good idea to rinse it under running water (the packer may have had a cold). Break the egg into a small bowl to check for small pieces of shell before slipping it into the pan. Remove the shell from a hard-boiled egg very carefully, making sure to remove all the little pieces that tend to stick. For your information, the color of the shell, brown or white, depends on the breed of hen. The egg inside either shell has the same nutritive value. The yolk of brown eggs may be a deeper yellow color, but this is only due to the kind of food in the chicken's diet. The food value is the same.

When cooking eggs in the shell always use an enamel or stainless-steel saucepan. Aluminum pans turn dark from boiling water and it takes a lot of scouring to get them shiny again.

III

Soft-boiled Egg

Place an egg in a small enamel saucepan and cover it with cold water. Bring water to a boil, reduce heat, and simmer gently for 4 minutes.

Remove egg from water and remove from shell into a small serving bowl. Break egg white into very small pieces with a spoon before feeding it to your baby. Yields 1 serving.

Coddled Egg

1 egg
2 tablespoons dry precooked cereal (optional)

Fill a small saucepan halfway with water. Bring water to a boil and lower the egg slowly into the boiling water, using a tablespoon. Turn off heat and cover the pan. Allow to stand for 6 minutes. Take egg from the water and remove it from the shell into a small serving bowl.

I occasionally add dry precooked cereal to the egg so that the yolk isn't quite so liquid. Mix until you have a smooth consistency. Yields 1 serving.

Poached Egg

1 egg
Water
2 tablespoons dry precooked cereal (optional)

Half-fill a small enamel saucepan with water and bring to a rapid boil. Break egg into a small cup and then pour it gently into the boiling water. Simmer the egg for about a minute. Lift it from the water with a slotted spoon. Place egg in a small bowl and break the white into very small pieces before serving.

If you would like the consistency of the yolk to be thicker, mix in 2 tablespoons of dry precooked baby cereal. Yields 1 serving.

Scrambled Egg

1 egg
1 tablespoon water
Milk

Break egg into a small bowl and add water. Beat well with a fork. Pour just enough milk into a small frying pan to cover the bottom. Heat until it bubbles around the edges. Turn the heat down very low. Pour egg into pan and stir continually until egg is softly scrambled. Break into small pieces before serving. Yields 1 serving.

Bacon and Egg

The bacon in this recipe must be *carefully* crushed into a fine paste. It adds a delicious flavor and interesting texture to the egg yolk.

1 egg
2 strips bacon
3 tablespoons milk

Put egg into a small enamel saucepan and cover with water. Bring to a rapid boil. Turn off heat and cover pan with a tight-fitting lid. Let stand for 20 minutes.

Remove cooked egg with a slotted spoon or tongs and immediately plunge into cold water to stop further cooking and to prevent the yolk from turning dark.

Shell egg very carefully, and remove any bits of shell that stick stubbornly to the white. Separate yolk from the white and press yolk through your food mill or a strainer. Discard the white.

Fry or broil bacon until very crisp. Drain well on a paper towel and place between two pieces of waxed paper. With a rolling pin, crush the bacon to a very fine paste. *Do not leave any solid bits of bacon; they may catch in the baby's throat.* Combine bacon, egg yolk, and milk in a small bowl and mix well. Yields 1 serving.

Gelatin, Puddings and Other Desserts

AT ABOUT FOUR MONTHS

Babies enjoy an occasional dessert. Gelatin and puddings are easy to make, and they keep everyday meals from getting monotonous. When the baby is between four and five months old, desserts won't add any new food element to his diet, but he will like the treat. And an occasional dessert does supply the nourishment of an extra egg, a little fruit, or a few more ounces of milk.

Your baby doesn't need a large variety of foods to assure proper nutrition, but if you add new tastes and textures when he is very young, you may not only avoid his growing up to be a "picky eater," but you can also help him take the step easily from baby foods to dinner with the family.

Many of the recipes that I originally made just for the baby turned out so well that I often increased the ingredients and served the same dessert to the entire family. These desserts are also fun to make because they bring back the memory of childhood tastes—baked custard, boiled puddings, tapioca.

Fruit Gelatin

Packaged gelatin desserts contain a number of additives, usually including artificial flavors and organic preservatives that increase their shelf-life. Since we're interested in the long-range health of our infants, and not the preservation of a twelve-cent package of dessert, I think we should take a few minutes to prepare our own fruit gelatin with ingredients that are full of natural flavors and nutrients.

1 envelope unflavored gelatin
¼ cup sugar
Pinch of salt
1½ cups of any fruit juice or combination of juices
½ cup water

Mix gelatin, sugar, and salt in a small saucepan. Add fruit juice and water. Place over low heat and stir until gelatin has dissolved. Pour into small serving bowls and chill until firm. Yields about 3 servings.
NOTE: If you use frozen fresh pineapple juice, first boil it for 2 minutes, then add other ingredients and stir, off the heat, until gelatin has dissolved.

Pineapple Whip

This dessert has such a fluffy texture that it will melt in your baby's mouth. It's also a snap to prepare, and you can substitute orange, apple, or cranberry juice for the pineapple juice whenever you want to vary it.

1 envelope unflavored gelatin
¼ cup sugar
Pinch of salt
1¾ cups canned fortified pineapple juice

Mix gelatin, sugar, and salt in a small saucepan. Then pour in pineapple juice. Place over low heat and stir until the gelatin has dissolved.

Chill until slightly thickened, then beat with a rotary beater or electric mixer until light and fluffy. Chill until firm. Yields about 4 servings.
NOTE: If you are making this dessert for grownups, add ½ teaspoon grated lemon rind after gelatin has dissolved.

Baked Custard

A custard can be a simple baked one, flavored with a sprinkle of nutmeg, or an elegant Crème Caramel.

2 eggs
2 egg yolks
3 tablespoons sugar
1/2 teaspoon vanilla
Pinch of salt
2 cups milk
Butter
Nutmeg (optional)

Preheat oven to 325°. Mix egg yolks, sugar, vanilla, and salt in a bowl. Mix well, but do not beat. Heat milk in a small saucepan until bubbles appear around the edges. Remove milk from heat and pour about a third of it into egg mixture; stir until well blended. Then pour egg mixture into remaining milk in the saucepan and stir again.

Butter 6 custard cups and set them in a shallow baking pan. Pour custard into cups and sprinkle it with a little nutmeg, if you like.

Pour enough hot tap water into the pan to reach halfway up the custard cups. Set pan in oven, being careful not to splash the water. Bake 35 minutes, then check custard by inserting a knife blade near the center of a custard cup. If the blade comes out shiny, the custards are done. If custard clings, bake 5 minutes more, then test again.

Remove pan from oven. Using tongs, lift custard cups out of the hot water. Cool before serving. Yields 6 servings.

Crème Caramel

Ingredients for Baked Custard (see preceding recipe)
1 cup sugar

Preheat oven to 325°. Prepare custard mixture.

Put sugar into a heavy saucepan or skillet and place over medium heat. Stir continually. Sugar lumps will melt as syrup forms. Remove melted sugar from heat when it is amber-colored and pour into a 1-quart baking dish. Using potholders, tip dish in all directions to form a glaze on the entire inside surface.

Pour custard mixture into baking dish and place dish in a shallow baking pan. Pour in enough hot tap water to reach halfway up the dish. Set pan carefully in the oven and bake for 1 hour. Test for doneness as described in the preceding recipe, and bake a few minutes longer if necessary. Remove baking dish from hot water and chill.

To serve, invert serving dish over the custard. Hold both dishes firmly together and turn them over to unmold the custard, now caramel-topped. Yields 6 servings.

Boiled Pudding

This quickie dessert takes about 10 minutes to make from start to finish. If you have a small portion of puréed fruit left over, but not enough for a serving, you can use it to garnish the pudding. And when your baby is older, this pudding makes a delicious topping for sponge or angel-food cake.

2 tablespoons sugar
1½ teaspoons cornstarch
⅛ teaspoon salt
1 egg
1 cup milk
½ teaspoon vanilla

Combine sugar, cornstarch, and salt in the top section of a double boiler. Mix in the egg, then gradually blend in the milk.

Set top over gently boiling water and stir constantly for 5 minutes. Cool slightly, then stir in vanilla. Spoon into custard cups. Yields 2 servings.

NOTE: Occasionally you'll get a few lumps in the pudding—perhaps the stirring wasn't constant enough. But whatever the reason, at one time or another it happens to all of us. Don't toss the pudding out—all is not lost. Pour the pudding through a fine strainer, using your cooking spoon to push it through the mesh. (Some of the best of cooks use this technique to remedy a lumpy gravy.)

Orange Fluff

This recipe is so good that you might like to double or triple the ingredients and serve the pudding to your whole family.

Juice of 1 orange, freshly squeezed
1 teaspoon lemon juice
1 egg yolk
2 teaspoons sugar
2 teaspoons arrowroot (if not available use cornstarch)
1 egg white, beaten stiff

Pour fruit juices through a very fine strainer. Beat egg yolk and sugar in a small bowl with a fork.

In a separate bowl, use 1 tablespoon of the juice to make a paste with the cornstarch. Add to the egg mixture, along with the remaining juices. Pour mixture into a small saucepan and set over low heat. Bring to a gentle boil, stirring and watching carefully; such a small amount boils quickly. Remove from heat. Cool for a few minutes and then stir again. Fold in the stiffly beaten egg white very gently. Serve cold. Yields 2 servings.

A Few Extra Recipes
for
the Five-Month-Old

Around five months of age your baby is probably chattering away to himself. Most of the time it is "Da-da, da-da, da-da" without regard for the fact that it is "Ma-ma, ma-ma, ma-ma" who changes his diapers and prepares his meals. He'll start grabbing for objects in earnest at this age, and he can usually grasp what he's going after.

At mealtime the objects of his attention will be the spoon and the feeding dish. There are many hazards involved in being a mother, but this is the messiest of them all. Try giving him a small rubber toy for each hand. This keeps both hands busy, and is not so distracting that he won't eat.

Because the following recipes don't seem to fit into any of my other categories, I have combined them in their own section. At five months your baby can enjoy his first pasta—in his case, pastina—and he is also old enough to have either plain or fruit yogurt, or cottage cheese mixed with honey and fruit. He'll enjoy milk toast, instead of cereal, for an occasional evening meal.

Pastina

This small, star-shaped noodle can be eaten as a side dish with only a little butter, or it can be mixed with a puréed vegetable or meat; or it can be mixed with a tablespoonful of milk or broth. It is an excellent choice for a texture between that of puréed foods and the chunkier junior foods. Pastina is so easy to swallow that your baby will hardly realize he's been asked to do anything new.

2 cups water
2 heaping tablespoons pastina
Pinch of salt

Bring water to a boil in a small saucepan. Pour in pastina and salt. Cook 5 to 7 minutes. Drain and serve in one of the ways mentioned above. Yields ¼ cup.

Cottage Cheese and Fruit

Use the creamy, bland, large-curd cottage cheese for your baby.

½ cup large-curd cottage cheese
1 teaspoon honey
1 tablespoon milk
2 tablespoons puréed fruit (pears, peaches, plums, or applesauce)

Purée all ingredients together in your blender or food mill until smooth. Yields about ⅔ cup.

Milk Toast

2 pieces zwieback or 1 slice toasted enriched bread
½ cup warmed milk
½ teaspoon honey or a sprinkle of sugar

Place zwieback in a cereal bowl and pour warm milk over it. Top with honey or sugar. Break toast into small pieces with a spoon before serving. Yields 1 serving.

Junior Foods

AT SEVEN TO EIGHTEEN MONTHS

At around the age of seven months you can slowly eliminate some puréed foods and start adding coarser textures—chopped fruits, vegetables, and meats. If you wait too long to make this change, your baby will already have some pretty set ideas and may be a bit finicky about chopped foods. However, though you want your baby to get used to chopped foods, *the shift must be a gradual one.* I think any baby would be quite annoyed to be eating smooth, puréed foods on Monday, and then be given a mouthful of lumps on Tuesday. So give him only a taste of very slightly chewy food at first.

Fruits and vegetables mash easily, so start by mashing, rather than puréeing, some of the baby's food. Give him small spoonfuls. Meats may be a little harder for him to handle because they need to be chewed. Continue to keep them almost smooth by using a meat grinder, or chop the meat for a few seconds in your blender.

If your baby doesn't have teeth, he can still handle chopped foods. He's able to perform a pretty fair mashing job with his gums. The most important thing is not to force chopped food on your baby. If he doesn't seem ready, wait a week and try again. Babies have a tricky way of gagging when mother starts getting pushy about new foods, and this may become a habit which is very difficult to break.

Many recipes in the preceding section can be adapted for the older baby, since the only difference between much of junior food and the infant's puréed food is consistency and seasoning. The basic ingredients are the same.

As your baby grows, continue to use the early recipes, but change the texture of the end product to a coarser version. This can easily be done by mashing the foods with a fork or putting them through a meat grinder, instead of using a blender.

junior cereal

Along with the smooth cereals that your baby is already eating, you can now give him well-cooked whole-grain cereal. It is coarser than Cream of Rice and farina and has much more flavor.

Wheatena or Ralston

½ cup water
2 tablespoons Wheatena
¼ teaspoon salt
Milk
Butter (about ½ teaspoon)
Sugar *or* honey (optional)

Bring water to a boil in a small saucepan and sprinkle in the cereal and salt. Cook over medium heat for 7 minutes, stirring occasionally.

Spoon into serving bowl, add butter, and allow to cool for several minutes. Then add a tablespoon or two of cold milk to the bowl. Add a sprinkle of sugar or honey, if you like. Always test the cereal to be sure it's not too hot for the baby. Yields about ½ cup.

---

bread and rolls

By the time your baby is nine months old, he may be pretty tired of cereal. Remember, it has been part of his diet for almost a year, and he certainly has a right to be bored. For a change, try whole-wheat, rye, oatmeal or toasted white, enriched bread or a bran or corn muffin. Babies also enjoy zwieback or an occasional baby cracker. Spread on a little puréed fruit (commercial jam is too sweet) or honey.

fruit

Until now, the only raw fruit that your baby has eaten has been mashed banana. It's time to add raw pears, apples, plums, and peaches.

Use only fully ripe fruits and wash them well. Your baby is still too young to eat the skins, so peel fruit, and be sure to remove all the seeds.

The peaches, plums, and pears can be easily mashed with a fork, and you can scrape the apple into a fine pulp with the point of a small spoon. If the rest of the family likes avocado, scrape off a little for the baby. To prevent darkening, prepare these fruits just before serving.

All the members of the berry family, from the strawberry to the wild blueberry, can be hard for babies to digest. This goes for cherries, too. It's best to wait until he is about a year and a half old before you give him berries and cherries. Wash berries well and mash them with a fork; otherwise your baby will swallow them whole and the berries will be passed the next day in the same shape they were eaten. Remove cherry pits.

At eighteen months your baby will also enjoy sweet, ripe melon. Wash melon, slice it, remove all seeds and cut the fruit away from the rind. Then find his largest bib—or a clean dishtowel would be great. Put it around his neck and hand your baby his piece of melon. Let him use his fingers, and as you watch him, you will realize that using a spoon would have taken away most of the good taste.

vegetables

During his first seven or eight months, your baby has had puréed peas, carrots, summer and winter squash, spinach, beets, celery, potatoes, tomatoes, parsnips, and green beans, either alone or in combinations. Continue to purée these vegetables, but on some days mash a part of a serving with a fork instead of puréeing all of it. Take five or six weeks to make the transition. By the end of that time, all of the baby's vegetables should be served mashed.

Add new vegetables—cauliflower, broccoli, green lima beans, asparagus, Brussels sprouts—and if your family likes turnips, give them a try too. Be prepared for an upturned nose at some new vegetables, but don't ruin a beautiful relationship by forcing something on the baby that he really dislikes. There is plenty of time for him to acquire a taste for things that are a bit unusual. Use frozen vegetables, following package instructions, when fresh ones aren't available. Do not overcook them and do not use canned vegetables.

When your baby is old enough for junior foods, he is also old enough for finger foods. These foods will encourage him to feed himself. Give him chunks of cooked carrots, string beans, or a soft meat, such as chicken or veal cutlet, cut into "baby-sized" bites. And don't worry about his lack of molars; his gums and tongue can mash the food. It may look like an unsightly mess to you, but unless he starts flinging food about with gay abandon, leave him alone to explore.

Broccoli

Use only the tops of the broccoli, as the stalks can be a bit stringy for a baby.

½ cup fresh broccoli tops, broken apart
Pinch of salt
½ teaspoon butter

Wash the broccoli well in cold running water. Place in a small saucepan and add enough water to cover. Add salt. Bring to a boil. Cover pan and simmer for 5 to 8 minutes just until tender. Drain. Mash well with a fork, and add butter. Yields ½ cup.

Cauliflower

When you cook fresh cauliflower for the family, break off a few flowerets and prepare them for the baby. A slice of lemon or a little lemon juice added to the cooking water helps keep the cauliflower white.

½ cup fresh cauliflower flowerets
Pinch of salt
Squeeze of lemon juice
½ teaspoon butter

Wash cauliflower well in cold running water. Boil about 1 inch of water in a small saucepan. Add salt, lemon juice, and cauliflower. Cook for 5 minutes uncovered, then cover. Cook for 5 to 10 minutes more, or just until tender. Drain. Mash well with a fork and add butter. Yields about ¼ cup.

Tomatoes Alexandria

1 ripe tomato
Butter (about 1 teaspoon)

Preheat the broiler. Wash tomato under running water and cut off 2 thin slices. Place tomato in a pan and top each tomato slice with a dab of butter. Broil about 3 inches from heat until butter bubbles and slices are soft. Mash well with a fork. Yields 1 serving.

Green Lima Beans

Choose the smallest lima-bean pods, because those will contain the tenderest beans.

½ pound fresh lima beans
Pinch of salt
2 slices bacon

Wash the lima beans under cold running water. Shell beans and place them in a small saucepan. Add salt and just enough water to cover. Bring to a boil, cover pan, and cook gently for 30 minutes, or until beans are tender. Drain. Mash well with a fork.

Meanwhile, fry or broil bacon until very crisp. Drain well and place between two pieces of waxed paper. With a rolling pin, crush the bacon to a very fine paste. *Do not leave any solid bits of bacon—they may catch in the baby's throat.* Sprinkle bacon over lima beans. Yields about ½ cup.

Brussels Sprouts

4 Brussels sprouts
Pinch of salt
1/2 teaspoon butter

Remove three or four of the outer leaves. Wash well under cold running water. Put into small saucepan with salt and just enough water to cover. Bring to a boil, cover pan, and simmer for 8 to 10 minutes or just until tender. Drain. Mash well with a fork and add the butter. Yields about 1/4 cup.

Asparagus Tips

Choose the bunch of asparagus with the most slender stalks. These will be the youngest and the tenderest.
6 stalks of asparagus
Pinch of salt
1/2 teaspoon butter

Cut the asparagus 3 inches from the tip, and discard the remaining part of the stem. (Though, of course, you wouldn't discard this much for adults.) Wash well under cold running water using a vegetable brush to remove any grains of sand. Place in a small saucepan with salt and enough water to cover. Bring to a boil, and cook for 5 to 8 minutes or just until tender. Drain. Mash with a fork and add the butter.

Turnips and Potatoes

Turnips puréed with potatoes to a consistency like that of mashed potatoes are delicious for the entire family.
1 small young turnip
1 small potato
1/4 teaspoon salt
1/2 teaspoon butter
1/4 cup milk

Wash, peel, and slice the turnip and potato. Place both in a small saucepan and add enough water to cover. Cover pan and boil gently for 20 to 30 minutes or until vegetables are fork-tender. Drain. Purée in a food mill or beat in an electric mixer. Add the salt and butter. Mix in the milk slowly. You may need more or less milk according to the size of the vegetables. Yields about 3/4 cup.

soups

Vegetable soup with a dessert, or cream of tomato soup with a bowl of fruit, is a pleasant change of pace from your baby's usual lunch or dinner.

Beef and Vegetable Soup

For a vegetable soup made with beef broth and without pieces of meat, you can use a batch of your own Beef Bouillon (page 103), plus the vegetables listed below. You'll need 2 cups of bouillon. Or make the beef stock as the following recipe directs, and include the meat in the finished soup.

Stock

½ pound beef chuck, in one piece
1 small carrot
1 rib celery
½ small onion
2 sprigs parsley
1 small tomato
3 cups water
½ teaspoon salt

Vegetables

You can add to the stock any fresh vegetables in season (except corn). A good soup can be made with the following vegetables:

Wipe beef with a damp paper towel. Wash vegetables. Scrape carrot and celery, peel onion, and quarter the tomato. Place beef in a saucepan and add water and salt. Bring to a boil, skimming off any froth. Add vegetables. Cover and simmer at low heat for an hour. If too much evaporates during cooking, add ½ cup water.

Strain the broth and reserve meat and broth. Discard vegetables. (After an hour of cooking, they have lost most of their vitamins and minerals.) Yields about 2 to 2½ cups of broth.

½ carrot
1 rib celery
1 tomato
¼ cup peas, fresh or frozen
3 to 5 green beans, fresh or frozen (¼ cup, cut up)
1 small potato
¼ cup young lima beans, fresh or frozen

Wash the fresh vegetables. Scrape the carrot and remove strings from celery. Quarter the tomato. Shell the peas and lima beans and snap off the ends of the green beans if they are fresh. Peel the potato. Dice the carrot, green beans, celery, and potato.

Return meat and broth to the sauce-pan and add the fresh vegetables. Cover and simmer for 30 minutes. Strain off and save the broth. Cut the meat into very small pieces, or grind it in the meat grinder. Mash vegetables well with a fork. Pour in enough of the broth to make a delicious soup for baby's lunch or dinner. Yields about $1\frac{1}{3}$ cups.

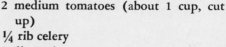

Cream of Tomato Soup

2 medium tomatoes (about 1 cup, cut up)
$\frac{1}{4}$ rib celery
1 slice onion
2 tablespoons water
1 teaspoon sugar
$\frac{1}{4}$ teaspoon salt
2 tablespoons butter
$1\frac{1}{2}$ tablespoons flour
1 cup milk

Wash vegetables. Remove the tomato skins by pouring over them enough boiling water to cover. Leave for $\frac{1}{2}$ minute and then plunge tomatoes immediately into cold water—the skin can be pulled off easily. Cut tomatoes into small pieces. Wash, scrape, and chop celery and peel the onion slice. Place tomatoes, celery, onion, water, sugar, and salt into a small saucepan and cover with a tight-fitting lid. Simmer for about 15 minutes.

Purée vegetables in your blender until very smooth. Make the cream sauce as follows. Over low heat, melt butter in a saucepan and blend in the flour. Then slowly stir in the milk. Cook and stir until thickened and smooth, about 5 minutes. Add the cream sauce to the tomato purée in the blender and blend for a few more seconds. Yields about 1¾ cups.

complete junior dinners

AT NINE TO TEN MONTHS

There are fewer recipes in this section because by nine or ten months your baby will be sharing more of the meals you've prepared for the family. When you put him in his high chair at the table, let him sample your pancakes, tuna-fish salad, or lemon meringue pie, even though he has eaten earlier. If you are out for a walk in the afternoon, let him have a bit of your ice-cream cone or a sip of your orange drink. He'll want to taste more and more of what you're eating, and unless it is highly spiced or really spiked with wine, let him share. If he can't share what you're having, give him a cracker as a substitute. There is nothing lonelier than watching everyone else enjoying a good meal and being left out.

The following recipes are one-dish meals designed for a baby nine to ten months—old enough to eat almost anything but still young enough to need chopped foods. Cook all the ingredients together, then serve the meat and vegetables separately, or combine them in a soup bowl for the baby's stew.

Chicken-Noodle Soup

For a quick version of this soup, you can use a batch of Chicken Broth (page 92) if you have it on hand (you'll need 1½ cups of broth), plus the noodles. Or make the stock this way, with a soup-bone added, and enrich the soup with chopped chicken.

½ breast ⎫
1 thigh ⎭ of a broiler-fryer chicken
1 veal shin bone, split
1 small carrot
1 rib celery
1 small piece (1 inch) parsnip
¼ small onion
2 sprigs parsley
2 cups water
¼ teaspoon salt
2 tablespoons very fine egg noodles

Remove the chicken skin and rinse the meat and the veal bone under running water. Wash vegetables. Scrape the carrot and parsnip. Remove celery strings. Peel the onion. Place the chicken, bone, and salt in a saucepan with the water and bring to a boil. Skim off any foam. Add vegetables, except the carrot. Cover the pan, but leave lid slightly to one side to allow the steam to escape. Simmer for 45 minutes, add the carrot and simmer 15 minutes more. Strain the broth through a sieve lined with cheese-cloth. Discard all the vegetables except carrot. Save the veal bone, too.

Pour about 1½ cups of the broth back into the saucepan, bring to a boil and add the egg noodles. Cook for about 10 minutes.

Put the chicken and carrot through a meat grinder, or chop them very fine. Mix meat and carrot with the broth and noodles—and lunch is ready. Yields about 1¾ cups.

Meatball Soup

This recipe can be found in the puréed-meats section on page 102. It makes a delicious junior dish when the meatballs are mashed with a fork instead of being puréed.

Brunswick Stew

This recipe is the basis for chopped chicken, either alone or with vegetables on the side, and for a one-pot dish of chicken and vegetables.

½ breast ⎤
1 thigh ⎦ of a broiler-fryer chicken
½ onion
1¾ cups water
½ small carrot
¼ cup green lima beans, fresh or frozen
1 small tomato, skinned
¼ teaspoon salt

Scrape and wash the carrot, and wash the lima beans if you're using fresh ones. Skin and quarter the tomato.

Remove skin from chicken and rinse meat under running water. Peel and wash onion slice. Put chicken, onion, and water in a saucepan.

Simmer, covered, for 30 minutes. Then add the tomato, carrot, lima beans and simmer 20 minutes more. If the broth is evaporating too fast, add another ¼ cup water. Discard onion. Strain the broth, but save the meat and the rest of the vegetables.

Put the chicken through a meat grinder or chop it very fine, and then mix in 6 tablespoons of the broth. Mash the vegetables together with 3 or 4 tablespoons of the broth. Yields about 2 cups.

For a one-pot dish, chop the chicken into very small pieces with a sharp knife. Mash the vegetables with a fork, and then spoon just enough broth (about 3 tablespoons) over the chicken and vegetables to make it easy for baby to eat. Yields about 1¾ cups.

Beef Stew

½ pound lean beef chuck (in 1-inch cubes)
1 small carrot
1 rib celery
½ small onion
2 sprigs parsley
1 small tomato, skinned
1 very small potato
¼ cup peas, fresh or frozen
2 cups water
½ teaspoon salt

Wipe the meat with a damp paper towel. Wash and scrape carrot and remove celery strings; cut both in half. Peel and wash onion slice. Wash parsley and tomato, then skin and quarter the tomato. Scrub, peel, and cut up the potato. Wash and shell peas, if fresh. If you are using frozen peas, it is not necessary to thaw them.

Brown meat on all sides in a hot heavy saucepan that has been greased very lightly with salad oil. Add water and salt and bring to a boil, skimming off any foam. Simmer for 1 hour. Add carrot, celery, onion, tomato, parsley, potato, and peas and simmer for 20 minutes more. Strain and reserve broth.

To serve as a three-dish meal (meat, vegetables, and potato), proceed as follows. Put meat and tomatoes through the meat grinder and stir in 5 or 6 tablespoons of broth. Mash the pieces of potato with 2 tablespoons of milk and a tiny slice of butter. Mash the peas, celery, onion, and carrots together with a fork. Yields about ¾ cup of meat, ¼ cup potato, and ⅔ cup vegetables.

Lamb Stew with Barley

As for the Beef and Barley Soup (page 101) use a fine barley when you make this stew. The pieces are tiny, but they will add an interesting taste and texture.

1 pound lamb shank with bone, cut in 3 or 4 pieces or ½ pound boned lamb shoulder, cut into 1-inch cubes
1 small tomato, skinned
3 to 5 fresh green beans
1 small carrot
2 sprigs parsley
2 cups water
1 slice onion
¼ teaspoon salt
1 tablespoon *fine* ready-to-cook barley

Trim all fat from the meat, then wipe it with a damp paper towel and pat dry. Rinse tomato, remove stem and cut in half. Wash green beans and snap in half, discarding the ends. Scrape and wash the carrot and wash the parsley.

Quickly brown the meat on all sides in a hot, heavy saucepan that has been greased very lightly with salad oil. Add water, salt, and onion, and bring to a boil, skimming off any foam. Simmer, covered, for one hour. Add the tomato, parsley, carrot, green beans, and barley and cook for 30 minutes more.

Strain the broth and save it.

Put the lamb through your meat grinder, then mix in 5 tablespoons of broth. Mash the vegetables and barley together with a fork. Yields about 2 cups.

Veal Ragout

This recipe is based on one of my own favorite stews. I'm very tempted to say, "Add ½ cup of this, and a tablespoon of that, and 1 garlic clove, and you'll have a delicious ragout for a Sunday-night get-together." But I won't. The next cookbook that I write will be for grownups, and I'll put back in all the ingredients that were taken out of these recipes.

½ pound stewing veal (shoulder or shin), cut into 1-inch cubes
1 veal shin bone, split if possible
1 small tomato, skinned
1 small potato
1 small carrot
1 medium mushroom (optional)
1 slice onion
¼ cup peas, fresh or frozen
2 cups hot water
2 sprigs parsley
¼ teaspoon salt
½ bay leaf

Trim off any fat from the meat. Wipe meat and veal bone with a paper towel and pat dry. Wash vegetables. Peel the potato, scrape the carrot, discard the stem of the mushroom, peel the onion slice and shell the peas, if fresh.

If you are using frozen peas, it is not necessary to thaw them. Brown meat and veal bone on all sides in a hot heavy saucepan that has been greased very lightly with salad oil. Add onion and water, bring to a boil, and skim off any foam. Add parsley and bay leaf. Simmer, covered, for 50 minutes. Add the potato, carrot, mushroom, tomato, and peas, and simmer 20 minutes more.

Grind the meat and mash the vegetables, discarding the bay leaf, and spoon everything back into the broth. Yields about 2 cups.

meats

When your baby is nine or ten months old, many of his meats will be a share of what you have prepared for the rest of the family. He can have meat loaf or a soft meatball if you mash them well with a fork. If you grind the baby's portion through your meat grinder, adding a little juice to moisten it, you can also serve him steaks and chops. Or you can cook liver or hamburger just for him.

Liver and Onion

1 small piece calf's liver (about 3 ounces)
1 tablespoon flour
1 tablespoon butter
Thin slice onion
4 tablespoons water

Wipe liver with a damp paper towel. Sprinkle flour on a piece of waxed paper and turn liver in it to lightly coat on both sides.

Melt butter in a frying pan and add liver and onion. Cook over a medium flame for about 3 minutes, then turn and cook 3 minutes more. Do not overcook. Liver should be a faint pink inside for tenderness and flavor.

Cut meat into very small pieces, removing any membrane, and put both liver and onion through the meat grinder.

Add water to the cooking juices in the pan and bring quickly to a boil. Spoon the pan gravy over the liver just before serving. Yields about ¾ cup.

Hamburger

Adding a slice of bread and some milk to the ground beef for the baby's hamburger is not merely an economy measure. It gives the hamburger a softer consistency.

½ slice white bread
2 tablespoons milk
3 ounces lean ground beef
Pinch of salt

Preheat broiler. Remove crust from bread and break bread into small pieces in bowl. Add milk and let stand for 5 minutes. Add ground beef and salt and mix well. Form gently into a patty and broil about 3 inches from the heat until cooked to the medium-done stage. Mash with a fork before serving. Yields 1 serving.

NOTE: Since no two broilers are exactly alike, I can't give you the exact cooking time. But by now you probably know the idiosyncrasies of your own broiler, so broil until the hamburger is cooked all the way through.

eggs

Babies love eggs, and what a boon that is for mothers! Don't hesitate to substitute eggs for meat in an occasional meal.

Many cooks, including me, use a special egg pan which is never used for anything else. I use a small one-egg frying pan just for cooking eggs for the baby. It's the perfect size, and as long as nothing else is cooked in it, the eggs will never stick.

Plain Omelet

Once you learn to make a perfect omelet, it will become your best friend. The recipe below is for a plain omelet of the classic French kind. Your baby will find it delicious.

1 egg
1 teaspoon cold water
Pinch of salt
1 teaspoon butter

Break egg into a small bowl and add water and salt. Beat with a fork just until well mixed. Melt butter in a small frying pan. When butter is hot, but not brown, add beaten egg. Stir around the edges with a fork, then stir a few times in the middle. As soon as the edges are cooked but while the top is still moist, start to fold the omelet. Using your fork, bring the right side toward the middle until the omelet is folded in half. Slip onto a plate, cut into small pieces, and serve. Yields 1 serving.

Cheese Omelet

After you have stirred the egg in the pan, sprinkle on about a tablespoon of grated American cheese. Fold and serve omelet. Yields 1 serving.

Bacon Omelet

Before you cook the omelet, fry or broil 2 strips of bacon *very crisp*. Drain well on a paper towel. Crumble the bacon into small pieces with your fingers. After you have stirred the egg in the pan, sprinkle it with crumbled bacon.

Fried Egg

A perfectly fried egg should be tender, yet firm; golden, but not browned on the bottom; have no hard edges; and have a shining, liquid yolk centered on the smooth white. If you don't achieve this perfection, your reputation will not be in jeopardy. The baby doesn't know these qualifications and he won't remember his early fried eggs when he's become a gourmet. By then, you will have improved your technique.

1 tablespoon butter
1 egg
Pinch of salt

Melt butter in a small frying pan. Carefully break the egg into a small bowl. Check to see that it is fresh (it should be odorless), that the yolk is unbroken, and that there are no pieces of shell. Slip the egg into the frying pan and turn the heat down very low. Cover pan and cook until egg matches the description above—or comes close to it. Place in serving dish and cut into very small pieces. Sprinkle with a pinch of salt. Yields 1 serving.

fish

AT ABOUT TEN MONTHS

Your baby can be given fish when he is about ten months old or whenever your doctor recommends it. I have found that babies seem to enjoy fish, not only for its delicate taste, but because it doesn't require much chewing.

Fish has the same amount of protein as meat. It has more phosphorus and calcium than meat, and contains a large amount of vitamins A and D. Such non-oily fish as cod, flounder, sole, and haddock are low in fat, which makes them easy to digest. Fish should be included in your baby's menu at least once a week. More often is even better.

Be sure the fish is fresh. If you are in any doubt about freshness, sniff the fish. It should be odorless, or almost so. If it smells fishy, don't buy it.

Always use fish the same day it is bought. Before cooking, rinse it under cold running water and pat it dry with a paper towel. Because fried fish is a little hard to digest, always bake, broil, or poach fish for your baby.

Before serving, go through the cooked fish with your fingertips (freshly washed for the occasion) to check for any bones. Even though the fish has been filleted, it is always possible for one small bone to be missed. Be most careful that *all bones* are removed.

Broiled Fish

The exact broiling time for this recipe will depend on your broiler. It's a good idea to check for doneness after 4 or 5 minutes if your broiler is a very efficient one—you don't want the fish to be overcooked and dry.

Salad oil
2- or 3-ounce fish fillet (flounder, sole, or any other non-oily white fish)
½ teaspoon lemon juice

Preheat the broiler. Line a small baking pan with aluminum foil and grease foil lightly with salad oil. Brush fish lightly with salad oil and sprinkle with lemon juice.

Broil about 3 or 4 inches from the heat for about 7 minutes, or until fish flakes easily with a fork. Do not turn. Place on serving dish and check *thoroughly* for bones. Flake into small bite-size pieces for the baby. Yields 1 serving.

Poached Fish

½ cup chicken broth
2- or 3-ounce fish fillet (flounder, sole, or any other non-oily white fish)
Sprig of parsley (optional)
½ teaspoon butter

Put broth into a saucepan and bring to a boil. Gently place fish in the broth. Add parsley, cover, and simmer gently for 9 to 10 minutes. Remove fish from the broth and dot with butter. (Because the broth is seasoned, there is no need for additional salt.) Place on a dish and check *thoroughly* for small bones. Flake into very small pieces. Yields 1 serving.

Baked Fish with Vegetables

2- or 3-ounce fish fillet (flounder, sole, or any other non-oily white fish)
½ small carrot
½ rib celery
1 small potato
1 cup water
Pinch of salt
Salad oil
½ teaspoon lemon juice
½ teaspoon butter
Chopped parsley (optional)

Wash and scrape carrot and celery. Remove celery strings. Scrub and peel the potato. Slice all the vegetables into very thin pieces. Pour water into a saucepan and bring to a boil. Add carrot and celery and boil for 15 minutes. Add potato and boil gently for 10 minutes more.

Preheat oven to 350°. Lightly grease a small baking dish with salad oil. Lift vegetables out of the broth, and place them in the baking dish.

Put the fish fillet on top of the vegetables and sprinkle with lemon juice. Dot with butter.

Add a little chopped parsley if you like—it adds to the appearance, and also contributes some vitamin C. Cover the dish with aluminum foil and bake for 15 minutes. Place fish and vegetables on a serving dish and check *thoroughly* for small bones. Cut fish into very small pieces. Mash vegetables well with a fork. Yields 1 serving.

desserts

Now that your baby has become accustomed to coarser meats and vegetables, the texture of junior foods can be carried over to his desserts.

Rice Pudding

½ cup precooked instant rice
1¼ cups plus 2 tablespoons milk
2 tablespoons sugar
1 teaspoon butter
Pinch of salt
1 egg yolk
½ teaspoon vanilla
Cinnamon

Combine rice, 1¼ cups of the milk, sugar, butter, and salt in a small saucepan and bring to a boil. Reduce heat to low and cook for 20 minutes, stirring frequently. In a small bowl, blend egg yolk with the remaining 2 tablespoons of milk. Slowly add to pudding (removed from the heat), stirring constantly. Add vanilla. Sprinkle with cinnamon. Serve at room temperature or chill. Yields 3 servings.

NOTE: For variety, cut about 2 tablespoons of raisins into small pieces, cover with boiling water and let stand for 20 minutes. Add raisins to pudding just before serving.

Tapioca Pudding

1½ tablespoons instant tapioca
2 tablespoons sugar
1 egg, beaten
1¼ cups milk
½ teaspoon vanilla
Pinch of salt

Mix all the ingredients except the vanilla in a small saucepan. Let stand for 5 minutes, then bring to a boil, stirring constantly. Remove from heat. Stir in the vanilla. Let stand at room temperature for 15 minutes. Then stir. Serve at room temperature or chill. Yields 3 servings.

Apples Ilana

This delicious dessert, named for (surprise!) my daughter, takes less than two minutes to prepare. There is only one trick—use a grater that gives the apple the consistency of applesauce. I use an old-fashioned potato grater, but any medium grater will do. Or you can "grate" the apple in the blender.

½ apple
¼ teaspoon lemon juice
½ teaspoon honey

Peel and wash apple. Make sure all seeds are removed. Pour lemon juice and honey into a small bowl, then grate apple directly into it. Mix well and serve. Yields ½ cup.

Baked Apple

2 small baking apples
2 tablespoons brown sugar
Pinch of cinnamon
2 small pats of butter
½ cup water
Raisins (optional)
Milk (optional)

Preheat oven to 375°. Remove peel from the upper third of the apples and cut out the cores, leaving hollows about 1 inch wide across. Fill each apple with 1 teaspoon sugar, a little cinnamon, and a pat of butter. You can also add some minced raisins at this point, or add them right after taking apples from the oven. Place apples in a small baking dish. Dissolve remaining sugar in the water and pour syrup around apples. Cover dish lightly with aluminum foil and bake for 1 hour.

Cool apples. For one serving, scoop out the pulp of one apple and mash it in a small dish with a fork. Discard apple skin. A few tablespoons of milk floating around the edges taste good too. Cover the other apple and store in the refrigerator. Yields 2 servings.

Orange Snow

1 envelope unflavored gelatin
½ cup sugar
Pinch of salt
2¼ cups water
1 can (10-ounce) frozen orange-juice
    concentrate
2 egg whites

Mix gelatin, sugar, and salt in a small saucepan. Add 1½ cups of the water. Place over low heat, stirring constantly, until gelatin has dissolved. Remove from heat and stir in the remaining ¾ cup of water and the frozen orange-juice concentrate. Continue stirring until frozen juice has melted. Chill until slightly thickened. Add egg whites and beat with a rotary beater until mixture begins to hold its shape. Chill before serving. Yields 4 servings.

NOTE: You can use any kind of frozen juice concentrate in this recipe, but fresh pineapple juice must be boiled for 2 minutes before adding or the dessert won't jell.

Floating Island

You probably remember this dessert from your childhood. If not, it's not too late to try it. The islands are not pieces of real estate but light, fluffy meringues. For dinner guests it becomes the very chic, very French Oeufs à la Neige.

Custard

3 egg yolks
1½ tablespoons sugar
Pinch of salt
1 cup milk
½ teaspoon vanilla

Mix egg yolks, sugar, and salt with a fork, but do not beat. Heat the milk in a heavy saucepan until bubbles form around the edges. Pour about a third of the milk into the egg mixture, stirring constantly. Then pour egg mixture back into the rest of the milk. Cook custard over low heat, stirring all the time with a metal spoon, until it is slightly thickened and coats the spoon. Do not let it boil or it will curdle. Remove from heat, add vanilla, and mix well. Pour into a shallow bowl and chill.

Meringue

1 cup milk
¼ teaspoon vanilla *or* a piece of vanilla bean
3 egg whites
4 tablespoons sugar

Pour milk into a small skillet and add vanilla. Warm over low heat until bubbles form around the edge.

Meanwhile, beat egg whites until foamy, then add the sugar a tablespoon at a time, continuing to beat until whites are stiff and stand up in sharp peaks. Drop large rounded tablespoons of the meringue into the simmering milk. It is easier to cook only two at a time. As soon as they set—in 2 or 3 minutes—lift meringues out carefully with a slotted spoon and place on top of the custard. Repeat until you have cooked all of the meringues. This should make six meringue "islands." Cool in refrigerator until ready to serve. Yields 3 servings.

drinks

As your child grows older—usually at about a year—he can manage a straw or a cup. At that time, you can occasionally give him one of the breezily named drinks in this section. Many of the canned and powdered fruit drinks that line the supermarket shelves have little nutritional value, are overly sweetened, and contain a long list of additives. Use one of the following recipes once in a while for a midafternoon drink. They are delicious and easy to make, and are a good source of extra milk and fruit. Some of these recipes make two servings, one for the baby and one for you. Remember, though, that these drinks are quite rich and should be used sparingly so neither you nor your baby will get fat.

Banana Smoothee

1½ cups milk
¼ teaspoon vanilla
1 tablespoon sugar *or* honey
1 large ripe banana, peeled and quartered

Whip all the ingredients in the blender, at high speed, for 20 seconds. Yields 2 servings.

Orange-Pineapple Flip

1 cup orange juice
2 slices canned pineapple, cut up
1 scoop (one well-rounded tablespoon) vanilla ice cream

Combine all ingredients in the blender jar and blend at high speed for 20 seconds. Yields 2 servings.

Banana Frosted

1 cup milk
1 scoop vanilla ice cream
1 ripe banana, peeled and quartered

Combine all ingredients in blender jar. Blend at high speed for 20 seconds. Yields 1 tall drink or 2 small servings.

Eggnog

¾ cup cold milk
½ teaspoon vanilla
1 egg
2 teaspoons sugar

Combine all ingredients in blender jar. Blend at high speed for 10 seconds. Yields 1 serving.

Pineapple Freeze

1½ cups canned pineapple juice
½ cup instant dry milk powder
2 scoops vanilla ice cream *or* pineapple
sherbet

Combine all ingredients in blender jar.
Blend at high speed for 10 seconds.
Yields 2 servings.

Orange-Cream Whiz

1 cup orange juice
2 scoops vanilla ice cream

Combine all ingredients in blender jar.
Blend at high speed for 10 seconds.
Yields 2 servings.

---

extra snacks

When your child has passed his first birthday and his diet has become more extensive, he is going to want to taste all the little extras (cheese wafers, corn curls, etc.) you keep in the kitchen for entertaining and snacks.

Cookies, pretzels, potato chips, and cakes are made up largely of starches, fats, and sugars, and are therefore very high in calories. These foods will quickly satisfy your baby's appetite and he will feel full, but he will not receive an iota of protein, vitamins, or minerals from them.

You have a great deal of control in the sweets-and-snacks department. Curb your own buying in these areas and your child will not think of them as everyday fare.

Carbonated drinks and candy, too, do not provide a child with any nutritional elements, and since they are usually between-meal treats, they spoil his appetite for the next meal. An occasional treat is nice for any child, but avoid sweets on a regular basis. Overly sweetened foods are also a hazard to healthy teeth.

Don't use sweets as a bribe to get your children to eat their vegetables—or to distract them or to keep them quiet. Let your child know that his dinner is just as good as ice cream. But don't be excessively rigid, either. A piece of birthday cake or some ice cream makes a wonderful dessert—once in a while. It's only when you permit a child to have a regular and steady diet of these foods that you deprive him of good nutrition and the child grows up with an insatiable sweet tooth.

Equivalents, or What Equals What

1 fluid ounce = 2 tablespoons
2 fluid ounces = 4 tablespoons = ¼ cup
4 fluid ounces = 8 tablespoons = ½ cup
8 fluid ounces = 1 cup
1 cup   = ½ pint   = 8 ounces
2 cups   = 1 pint   = 16 ounces
4 cups   = 1 quart   = 32 ounces
⅓ cup   = 5 tablespoons + 1 teaspoon
3 teaspoons   = 1 tablespoon
1 medium lemon yields about 3 tablespoons juice
1 medium orange yields 6–8 tablespoons juice
¼ pound butter = ½ cup = 1 stick
1 pound of peas in the pod yields 1 cup of shelled peas
A pinch is all you can pick up between your thumb and forefinger.

Index

About the Author

RUTH PEARLMAN is the mother of a baby girl and an eleven-year-old boy. She is also a brilliant young scientist who has done important research as a biophysicist and has designed and built complex scientific apparatus now in commercial production. She is now living, "on sabbatical" with her husband and children, in a small village on the Italian coast.